Collins

Level 6, Boos

GW00341265

NEW MATHS FRAMEWORKING

Building process skills for KS3 and GCSE

Chris Pearce

Introduction

Welcome to *New Maths Frameworking*!

This workbook aims to help you reach a Level 6 in maths at Key Stage 3 and has hundreds of levelled questions to give you plenty of practice in the main areas of your course:

Number

Algebra

Shape, space and measure

Data handling

Smooth progression
Each topic allows you to practise your skills at Level 5 before moving on to try lots of Level 6 questions.

Levelled questions
Colour-coded National Curriculum levels for all the questions show you what level you are working at so you can easily track your progress and see how to get to the next level.

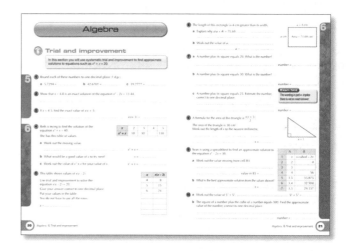

Review
The handy reviews at the end of each section let you assess your understanding of a mixture of topics.

Exam hint
Avoid common mistakes and remember the key points of a topic with the useful 'Exam hint' boxes.

Level progression maps
At the back of the book are level progression maps for the main subject areas. These show how you can move from a Level 5 to a Level 6 in each one. Use them to check what you know and what you need to practise more!

Answers
Finally there are answers to all the questions at the back of the book. You can check your answers yourself or your teacher might tear them out and give to you later to mark your own work.

William Collins' dream of knowledge for all began with the publication of his first book in 1819. A self-educated mill worker, he not only enriched millions of lives, but also founded a flourishing publishing house. Today, staying true to this spirit, Collins books are packed with inspiration, innovation and practical expertise. They place you at the centre of a world of possibility and give you exactly what you need to explore it.

Collins. Freedom to teach.

Published by Collins
An imprint of HarperCollins*Publishers*
77–85 Fulham Palace Road
Hammersmith
London
W6 8JB

© HarperCollins*Publishers* Limited 2011

10 9 8 7 6 5 4 3 2 1

ISBN-13 978-0-00-743808-2

British Library Cataloguing in Publication Data
A Catalogue record for this publication is available from the British Library.
Commissioned by Katie Sergeant
Project managed by Emma Braithwaite
Edited by Joan Miller
Answers checked by Kay Macmullan and Joan Miller
Proofread by Joan Miller and Chris Pearce
Concept design by Jordan Publishing Design Limited
Design and typesetting by Hedgehog Publishing Ltd
Illustrations by Ann Paganuzzi
Cover design by Julie Martin
Production by Arjen Jansen
Printed and bound by Martins the Printers, Berwick upon Tweed

Browse the complete Collins catalogue at: www.collinseducation.com

Acknowledgements

The publishers wish to thank the following for permission to reproduce photographs. Every effort has been made to trace copyright holders and to obtain their permission for the use of copyright material. The publishers will gladly receive any information enabling them to rectify any error or omission at the first opportunity.

Cover image: The top end of a large crane ©shutterstock.com/Shi Yali

Contents

Number

1 Percentages

In this section you will calculate percentages and find the outcome of a given percentage increase or decrease.

1 Calculate the following. Do not use a calculator.

  a 25% of £30 = £.......................................

  b 10% of 250 kg = ...kg

  c 75% of 82 = ...

  d 5% of £350 = £...................................

  e 90% of £2.50 = £.......................................

  f 5% of 6000 = ...

2 Use a calculator to find these percentages.

  a 28% of £43 = £.......................................

  b 73% of £160 = £...................................

  c 3.5% of £4500 = £.......................................

3 The population of a village was 800 people. It increases by 15%.

  a What is the increase in population? ....

  b What is the new population? ....

4 The cost of a plane ticket has increased by 30%. It was originally £180.

  a What is the increase in price? .... £.................

  b What is the new price? .... £.................

5 Calculate the new amount after the following increases.

  a A price of £250 is increased by 40%. ....

  .... New price = £................

  b A mass of 32 kg is increased by 65%. ....

  .... New mass = ...kg

6 The price of a second-hand car was £1800. In a sale this was reduced by 20%.

    a What was the reduction in price? ....

    ....

    .... £..............

    b What was the sale price? ....

    ....

    .... £..............

7 In a sale prices are reduced by the percentage shown. Find the sale price in each case.

    a Shirt, price was £28.00, reduced by 25% ....

    ....

    .... Sale price = £..............

    b Jacket, was £96.00, reduced by 40% ....

    ....

    .... Sale price = £..............

8 A restaurant adds a 12% service charge onto the cost of a meal.
A meal costs £65.85 before the service charge is added.

    a Work out the service charge. ....

    .... £..............

    b Work out the total bill. ....

    .... £..............

9

PRICES DOWN BY AT LEAST 40%!

SUIT WAS £179.99 NOW ONLY £119.99

Is the claim correct? Give a reason for your answer.

....

....

Exam hint

Reasons should include numbers or calculations.

10 Here are the prices of three items in a sale.

Item	Original price	Sale price
Television	£525	£450
Computer	£649	£449
Camera	£285	£229

State whether each item has been reduced by **more** or **less** than 25%. Give a reason for your answer in each case.

Television ....

....

Computer ....

....

Camera ....

....

11 In 1950 the population of a town was 12 000. By 1995 it had risen by 150%. What was the population of the town in 1995?

....

.... Population ....

12 In 2009 the cost of Jasmine's car insurance was £400.

a It went up by 20% in 2010. Explain why the cost in 2010 was £480.

....

....

b It went up by another 20% in 2011. Explain why the cost in 2011 was £576.

....

....

13 Alan's ticket for a concert cost £32. Simon's cost 50% more than Alan's. Becky's cost 50% less than Simon's. What did Becky's ticket cost?

....

.... £................

② Fractions, decimals and percentages

In this section you will use the equivalence of fractions, decimals and percentages to compare proportions.

① Put these in order, starting with the smallest. $\frac{3}{4}$ 0.6 $\frac{2}{3}$ 0.58

.... < .... < .... < ....

② Write these decimals as fractions, as simply as possible.

a 0.7 = ...   **b** 0.05 = ...

c 1.2 = ...

③ Write these fractions as decimals.

a $\frac{4}{5}$ = ...   **b** $\frac{7}{50}$ = ...

c $3\frac{1}{4}$ = ...

④ Write these percentages as fractions and simplify them as much as possible.

a 80% = ...   **b** 150% = ...

c 2.5% = ...

⑤ Write these fractions as percentages. Round them to 1 decimal place if necessary.

a $\frac{2}{5}$ = ...%   **b** $\frac{3}{8}$ = ...%

c $\frac{2}{3}$ = ...%   **d** $\frac{4}{9}$ = ...%

e $\frac{17}{24}$ = ...%   **f** $\frac{5}{32}$ = ...%

⑥ Write these decimals as percentages.

a 0.4 = ...   **b** 0.63 = ...

c 0.175 = ...   **d** 0.07 = ...

e 1.4 = ...   **f** 2.25 = ...

7 There are 80 people in a choir and 48 of them are women.

  a What fraction of the choir are women? ....

  b What percentage of the choir are men? ....%

8 There are 6517 in a town and 2481 are children.

  a What percentage are children? ....%

  b What percentage are adults? ....%

9 This table shows the numbers of employed and unemployed adults in two towns.

Town	Employed adults	Unemployed adults	Total
Aberdale	4352	1238	5590
Berryton	6704	1512	8216

A newspaper article says that unemployment is worse in Berryton than in Aberdale.

Exam hint

Use percentages.

Is this correct?

You must give reasons for your answer and quote figures to justify it.

....

....

....

....

10 These are the headlines in three newspapers.

More than 30% say 'Yes' to cinema	70% SAY 'NO!' TO CINEMA PLANS	One in three in favour of new cinema

Can they all be correct? Give a reason for your answer.

....

....

....

11 These are the prices for tickets to a cup final.

The decision is taken to reduce all prices by £10.
What is the percentage saving on each ticket?

West stand	£35.00
Centre stand	£45.00
East stand	£70.00

West stand ....

....%

Centre stand ....

....%

East stand ....

....%

12 Over ten years the value of a vintage car increased from £2400 to £4600.

What is the percentage increase in value? ....

....%

13 Here are the prices made at auction by three items 10 years ago and this year.

Item	10 years ago	This year
Painting	£560	£800
Table	£1250	£975
Vase	£325	£750

Calculate the percentage increase or decrease for each item.

Painting ....

....%

Table ....

....%

Vase ....

....%

③ Ratio

In this section you will divide a quantity into two or more parts in a given ratio and solve problems involving direct proportion and ratio.

① 5 In a gymnastics club the ratio of boys to girls is 2 : 1. There are 16 boys. How many girls are there?

.... girls

② In a box of chocolates there are 8 creams and 12 toffees. Write the ratio of creams to toffees as simply as possible.

.... creams : toffees = ... : ....

③ 6 One morning during the rush hour 140 cars and lorries pass by. The ratio of cars to lorries is 3 : 1. How many cars pass by?

.... cars

④ A bag contains counters that are red or blue. The ratio of red counters to blue counters is 3 : 2. There are 180 red counters in the bag. How many blue counters are in the bag?

.... blue counters

⑤ A recipe uses flour and butter in the ratio 3 : 1. How much butter is needed to mix with 450 grams of flour?

.... grams

⑥ Arturo and Bella share £600 in the ratio 1 : 4.

   a How much does each one receive?

....

.... Arturo £............. Bella £.............

   b What fraction of the money does Arturo receive? ....

   c What percentage of the money does Bella receive? ....%

⑦ The first, second and third places in a golf competition share £5000 prize money in the ratio 5 : 3 : 2. How much does each receive?

....

.... First £............. Second £............. Third £.............

8 The ages of Sally and Nathan are in the ratio 3 : 5. Nathan is 30 years old.

   a How old is Sally?

   .... years old

   b What will the ratio of their ages be in six years' time? ....

   .... : ....

9 Natalie, Sam and Carrie share some money in the ratio 6 : 3 : 1.

   a What fraction of the money does Sam get?

   ....

   b What percentage of the money do Sam and Carrie get between them?

   ....

10 Alice, Chloe and Zeta are playing a game in which they score points. The ratio of their points is 3 : 5 : 6. Chloe has 45 points. How many points do the others have?

   ....

   .... Alice .... points   Zeta .... points

11 Three people share the cost of a holiday between them.

   Lucy pays $\frac{1}{2}$, Gary pays $\frac{1}{3}$ and Mary pays $\frac{1}{6}$.

   What is the ratio of their three shares?

Exam hint

The total cost is not given. You can choose your own if you wish.

   ....

   ....

   .... Lucy : Gary : Mary = ... : .... : ....

12 Frankie and Johnnie put their money together. They have £60 and $\frac{3}{4}$ was Frankie's.

   a What is the ratio of their shares?

   ....

   .... Frankie : Johnnie = ... : ....

   b Each of them is given another £20. What is the ratio of their shares now?

   ....

   .... Frankie : Johnnie = ... : ....

4 Proportional reasoning

In this section you will use proportional reasoning to solve a problem, using the correct number to take as a whole, or as 100%.

1 Liz has saved £60. She spends £24. What percentage of her savings has she spent?

....%

2 Lauren walks 3 kilometres in 30 minutes. If she continues at the same speed, how far will she walk in 3 hours?

.... kilometres

3 A baby is weighed at three different times. The first time her mass is 3.8 kilograms. The second time it is 4.0 kilograms. The third time it is 4.2 kilograms. What is the overall percentage increase?

....%

4 Andy spends £8400 per year on rent. This is $\frac{1}{3}$ of his annual salary. What is his annual salary?

.... £.......................

5 In 2011 the population of Wales reached 3 million for the first time. This is 5% of the population of the UK. Find the UK population.

....

6 Ray is trying to lose weight. He weighs himself at the end of each month.

Time	End of March	End of April	End of May
Mass (kg)	114.5	109.3	102.7

Calculate these percentage weight losses, correct to one decimal place.

a In April ....%

b In May ....%

c From the end of March to the end of May ....

....%

7 A recipe for four people uses 500 grams of pasta, two eggs and 300 grams of tomatoes. How much of each ingredient will be needed for ten people?

....

.... pasta .... eggs .... tomatoes

8 A packet of breakfast cereal has a mass of 375 grams and contains 255 grams of rice flakes.

a What will be the mass of rice flakes in a 30 gram serving of cereal?

....

.... grams

b A 30 gram serving of cereal requires 125 millilitres of milk.
How much milk is needed for the whole packet?

....

....litres

9 A bottle of fruit cordial recommends that it is diluted with water in the ratio 1 to 10. The bottle holds 500 millilitres of cordial.

Exam hint

You should remember how many ml there are in 1 litre.

a How many litres of drink will the bottle make?

....

.... litres

b The label says that the bottle will make 22 servings. How big is a serving?

....ml

10 In a sale there was a 25% discount on a pair of shoes. Lizzie paid £45 for the shoes.
What was the price of the shoes before the sale?

.... £............

11 Mr Smart is buying a second-hand car. He pays a 20% deposit of £1500.
What is the price of the car?

....

.... £............

12 Gemma is making concrete. She uses the following ingredients, by volume.

1 part cement $\frac{1}{2}$ part water

$2\frac{1}{2}$ parts sand $2\frac{1}{2}$ parts gravel

a How many buckets of concrete can she make if she has two buckets of cement?

.... buckets

b How many litres of concrete can she make from 25 litres of sand?

.... litres

13 Rich's job is collecting items from supermarket shelves for delivery to customers. His target is to collect 10 items every five minutes. How long should he take to collect 48 items?

.... minutes

⑤ Calculating with fractions

In this section you will:
- add and subtract fractions by writing them with a common denominator
- calculate fractions of quantities, which may have fraction answers
- multiply and divide a fraction by an integer.

Do not use a calculator in this section.

1 Write these fractions as simply as possible.

     a $\frac{8}{12} =$ ....

     b $\frac{15}{40} =$ ....

     c $\frac{12}{16} =$ ....

2 Write these fractions as mixed numbers.

     a $\frac{7}{2} =$ ....

     b $\frac{7}{4} =$ ....

     c $\frac{16}{3} =$ ....

3 Complete these additions.

     a $\frac{1}{2} + \frac{1}{4} =$ ....

     b $\frac{1}{2} + \frac{3}{8} =$ ....

     c $\frac{1}{2} + \frac{2}{5} =$ ....

     d $\frac{3}{8} + \frac{1}{6} =$ ....

4 Out of 48 people on a coach, $\frac{1}{3}$ were men, $\frac{1}{4}$ were women and the rest were children. What fraction were children?

....

....

5 Here is an incorrect calculation. $\frac{1}{3} + \frac{1}{5} = \frac{1+1}{3+5} = \frac{2}{8} = \frac{1}{4}$

Write a correct version.

....

....

6 Annie jogged $2\frac{1}{2}$ miles. She rested, then jogged another $1\frac{3}{4}$ miles. How far did she jog altogether?

.... miles

7 Complete these additions, giving your answers as mixed numbers.

     a $\frac{3}{4} + \frac{5}{8} =$ ....

     b $\frac{2}{3} + \frac{7}{12} =$ ....

     c $1\frac{1}{2} + \frac{2}{3} =$ ....

     d $\frac{5}{8} + \frac{11}{12} =$ ....

8 Complete these subtractions.

a $\frac{3}{4} - \frac{2}{3} =$ ....

b $1\frac{1}{2} - \frac{5}{8} =$ ....

c $1\frac{3}{8} - \frac{7}{12} =$ ....

9 Of the people in a survey, $\frac{3}{4}$ had a cat, and $\frac{1}{6}$ had both a cat and a dog.
What fraction had a cat but not a dog?

....

10 Find these amounts, giving your answers as mixed numbers.

a $\frac{1}{3}$ of 10 = ...

b $\frac{1}{4}$ of 15 = ...

c $\frac{1}{5}$ of 13 = ...

d $\frac{1}{8}$ of 22 = ...

11 Find these amounts, giving your answers as mixed numbers.

a $\frac{2}{3}$ of 8 = ...

b $\frac{3}{4}$ of 26 = ...

c $\frac{3}{5}$ of 9 = ...

d $\frac{5}{8}$ of 6 = ...

12 Ten people each ate $\frac{1}{3}$ of a pizza. How many pizzas were eaten altogether?

.... pizzas

13 Complete these calculations.

a $5 \times \frac{3}{4} =$ ....

b $6 \times \frac{2}{5} =$ ....

c $4 \times \frac{7}{8} =$ ....

14 Complete these calculations.

a $3 \div \frac{1}{2} =$ ....

b $6 \div \frac{3}{4} =$ ....

c $5 \div \frac{2}{3} =$ ....

15 Beth said that $6 \div \frac{1}{2}$ is 3 because a half of 6 is 3.
How would you convince Beth that the correct
answer is 12?

> **Exam hint**
> This is a very common mistake.
> Make sure you do not make it!

....

....

16 Carla and Nicolas agree that $4 \div \frac{1}{3} = 12$.

Carla thinks that therefore $4 \div \frac{2}{3} = 6$ but Nicolas thinks that $4 \div \frac{2}{3} = 24$.
Who is correct? Give a reason for your answer.

....

1 Here are the populations of three towns in two different years.

Year	Albury	Bishford	Calsten
1980	3400	39 200	12 700
2000	6500	45 100	17 400

Compare the way the populations of the three towns changed between 1980 and 2000. Which has changed most? Which has changed least? Make any calculations you need to illustrate your comments.

....

....

....

....

....

2 Do not use a calculator in this question.

a Work out the following.

$\frac{1}{2} - \frac{1}{3} =$ .... $\frac{1}{3} - \frac{1}{4} =$ .... $\frac{1}{4} - \frac{1}{5} =$ ....

b Now try to continue the pattern of part **a**.

....

....

....

c What happens if the – signs in part **a** are changed to + signs?

....

....

....

3 **a** Show that $\frac{5}{8}$ is bigger than $\frac{3}{5}$ and smaller than $\frac{7}{10}$.

....

....

b Find a fraction that is between $\frac{1}{5}$ and $\frac{1}{3}$. Justify your answer.

....

....

4 VAT is a tax that is added to the price of many items when they are sold.

On 4 January 2011 the rate of VAT was increased from 17.5% to 20%.

  a A garage bill, before VAT was added, was £200.

    i What was the total bill before 4 January?

    .... £.........................

    ii What was the total bill after 4 January?

    .... £.........................

  b Show that the effect of the change in the rate of VAT was to increase the bill by about 2.1%.

    ....

    ....

5 | A speed of 5 miles per hour is about the same as 8 kilometres per hour.

  a In Britain the national speed limit is 70 miles per hour. In New Zealand the national speed limit is 100 kilometres per hour.

    Which of these is faster? Give a reason for your answer.

    ....

    ....

  b Use the fact in the box to change some common British speed limits into kilometres per hour. Present your results in any way that makes them easy to read.

    ....

    ....

    ....

    ....

6 **a** The ratio of the three angles of a triangle is 2 : 3 : 4.

    What are the angles of the triangle?

    ....

    ....

    .... The angles are ....

  b Suppose the ratio of the three angles of a triangle is $x : y : z$ and one of the angles is 90°.

    What can you say about the numbers x, y and z? Give a reason for your answer.

    ....

    ....

Algebra

(6) Trial and improvement

In this section you will use systematic trial and improvement to find approximate solutions to equations such as $x^3 + x = 20$.

5

(1) Round each of these numbers to one decimal place (1 d.p.).

a $5.7294 \approx$ ....

b $42.6701 \approx$ ....

c $19.7777 \approx$ ....

(2) Show that $x = 4.8$ is an exact solution of the equation $x^2 - 2x = 13.44$.

....

(3) If $x = 4.5$, find the exact value of $x(x + 3)$.

.... $x(x + 3) =$ ....

6

(4) Beth is trying to find the solution of the equation $x^3 + x = 40$.

She has this table of values.

x	2	3	4	5
$x^3 + x$	10	30		130

a Work out the missing value.

.... $x^3 + x =$ ....

b What would be a good value of x to try next? $x =$ ....

c Work out the value of $x^3 + x$ for your value of x. $x^3 + x =$ ....

(5) This table shows values of $x(x - 2)$.

Use trial and improvement to solve the equation $x(x - 2) = 20$.
Give your answer correct to one decimal place.
Put your values in the table.
You do not have to use all the rows.

$x =$ ....

x	$x(x - 2)$
4	8
5	15
6	24

6 The length of this rectangle is 4 cm greater than its width.

a Explain why $a(a + 4) = 71.69$. ....

....

b Work out the value of a. ....

.... $a =$ ....

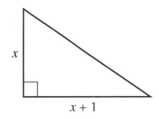

$a + 4$ cm

a cm | Area = 71.69 cm²

7 a A number plus its square equals 20. What is the number?

.... number = ...

b A number plus its square equals 30. What is the number?

.... number = ...

Exam hint

The wording in part **c** *implies* there is not an exact answer.

c A number plus its square equals 25. Estimate the number, correct to one decimal place.

....

.... number = ...

8 A formula for the area of this triangle is $\dfrac{x(x + 1)}{2}$.

The area of the triangle is 30 cm².
Work out the length of x to the nearest millimetre.

....

.... $x =$ ....

x

$x + 1$

9 Sean is using a spreadsheet to find an approximate solution to the equation $x^3 - 2x = 30$.

a Work out the value missing from cell B3.

....

.... value in B3 = ...

b What is the best approximate solution from the values shown?

.... $x =$ ....

	A	B
1	x	x cubed – $2x$
2	2	4
3	3	
4	4	56
5	3.5	35.875
6	3.4	32.504
7	3.3	29.337

10 a Work out the value of $5^2 + 5^3$. .... $5^2 + 5^3 =$ ....

b The square of a number plus the cube of a number equals 300. Find the approximate value of the number, correct to one decimal place.

....

.... number = ...

7 Linear equations

In this section you will construct and solve linear equations with integer equations, using an appropriate method.

1 The lengths of the sides of a triangle are x cm, $x + 1$ cm and $x + 2$ cm. Write down an expression for the perimeter of the triangle, simplifying it as much as possible.

.... perimeter = ... cm

2 Write the expression $2(3a - 4)$ without brackets.

....

3 A formula for changing miles (M) into kilometres (K) is $= \dfrac{8M}{5}$.

How many kilometres is 20 miles? ....

.... km

4 Solve these equations.

a $3a - 15 = 24$ ....

.... $a =$ ....

b $4(d + 2) = 30$ ....

.... $d =$ ....

c $5 = 4m + 13$ ....

.... $m =$ ....

d $30 - 2r = 7$ ....

.... $r =$ ....

e $23 = 8 - 3e$ ....

.... $e =$ ....

f $\dfrac{2f - 5}{7} = 9$ ....

.... $f =$ ....

5 Solve the equation $3x + 12 = 5x - 21$.

....

.... $x =$ ....

6 Solve the equation $2(y - 3) + 3(y - 8) = 0$.

....

.... $y = $ ....

7 The width of a rectangle is w cm. The length is 6 cm greater than the width.

  a Write the length of the rectangle in terms of w. length = ...

  b Show that the perimeter of the rectangle is $4(w + 3)$ cm.

  ....

  ....

  c The perimeter of the rectangle is 27 cm. Work out the value of w.

  ....

  ....

  .... $w = $ ....

8 The cost (£C) of hiring a coach for a journey of K km is given by the formula $C = 4K + 35$.
If the cost was £563, how long was the journey?

.... km

9 Solve these equations.

> **Exam hint**
>
> In questions like this, remove the fraction first.

  a $\dfrac{4}{x} = 8$

  .... $x = $ ....

  b $\dfrac{x + 10}{x} = 3$

  .... $x = $ ....

  c $\dfrac{x}{x - 3} = 6$

  .... $x = $ ....

10 A formula for converting from degrees Celsius (C) to degrees Fahrenheit (F) is $F = \dfrac{9C + 160}{5}$.

  a Change 50°C into °F.

  ....°F

  b Change –4°F into °C.

  ....°C

  c x°C is the same as x°F. What is the value of x?

  ....

  .... $x = $ ....

Sequences

In this section you will:
- use term-to-term and position-to-term definitions of a sequence
- write an expression for the *n*th term of an arithmetic sequence.

1 If $n = 5$, work out:

   a $3n + 4$ ....   **b** $3(n + 4)$ ....

   c $3 - 4n$ ....   **d** $n^2 + 3$ ....

2 If $n = 4$, work out:

   a $n(n + 2)$ ....   **b** $(n + 3)^2$ ....

3 To generate a sequence you start with 50 and subtract 4 each time. The first term is 50.

   a The 5th term is ....   **b** The 10th term is ....

4 1   2   4   8   ...

The term-to-term rule for this sequence is 'multiply by 2'.

   a Find the 6th term.

   .... 6th term = ...

   b Complete this sentence.

   The first term that is bigger than 200 is the ....th term.

5 13   10   7   4   ...

   a What is the term-to-term rule for this sequence?

   ....

   b Find the 10th term.

   .... 10th term = ...

6 A spreadsheet is used to generate a sequence, using a position-to-term rule.

   a What number is missing from cell B5?

   ....

   ....number in cell B5 = ...

   b The formula in cell B4 is = A4*3 + 4
   What is the position-to-term rule?

   ....

	A	B
1	position	term
2	1	7
3	2	10
4	3	13
5	4	
6	5	19

7 The nth term of a sequence is $n + 8$.

   a Find the 4th term.

   ....   4th term = ...

   b Which term is the number 20?

   ....th

8 The nth term of a sequence is $40 - 5n$.

Is 0 in this sequence? Give a reason for your answer.

....

9 The nth odd number is $2n - 1$.

   a What is the 200th odd number? ....   200th odd number = ...

   b Write down a formula for the nth even number. nth even number = ...

10 The term-to-term rule for a sequence is 'add 3'. Which of these could be the nth term?
Circle each possible answer.

   $n + 3$ $3n$ $3n - 3$ n^3 $3n + 6$

11 The nth term of a sequence is $n(n + 1)$. Write down the first four terms.

....

12 The nth term of a sequence is $2n^2$. Sam writes: The 10th term is $2 \times 10^2 = 20^2 = 400$.

This is not correct. Write a corrected version.

....

Exam hint

Can you use the answer to
part **a** to help with part **b**?

13 **a** 5   10   15   20   ...

      Find the nth term of this sequence.

      .... nth term = ...

   b 3   8   13   18   ...

      Find the nth term of this sequence. .... nth term = ...

14 10   14   18   22   ...

Find the nth term of this sequence. .... nth term = ...

15 100   94   88   82   ...

Find the nth term of this sequence. .... nth term = ...

Straight-line graphs

In this section you will:
- plot the graphs of linear functions, where y is given explicitly in terms of x.
- recognise that equations of the form $y = mx + c$ correspond to straight-line graphs.

5

1 **a** Write down the coordinates of the lettered points.

A(....., ...)   B(....., ...)

C(....., ...)   D(....., ...)

b Find the equations of lines L and M.

L ....

M ....

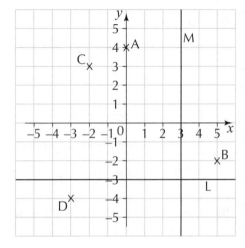

6

2 **a** Complete this table of values for $y = 2x - 1$.

	−3	−1	0	2	3
		−3			5

b On the graph, draw the line $y = 2x - 1$.

c Complete this table of values for $y = 5 - x$.

	−3	−1	0	1	3
		6			2

d On the same graph draw the line $y = 5 - x$.

e Where do the lines cross?

The lines cross at ....

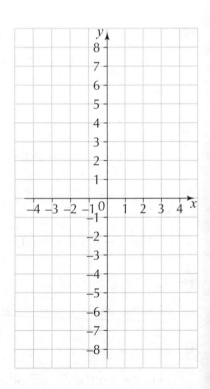

3 a Complete this table of values for $y = x + 4$.

x	−3	−1	0	1	3
y				5	

b Complete this table of values for $y = 1 - 2x$.

x	−3	−1	0	1	3
y				−1	

c On the graph draw the line $y = x + 4$ and $y = 1 - 2x$.

d Where do the lines cross?

The lines cross at ....

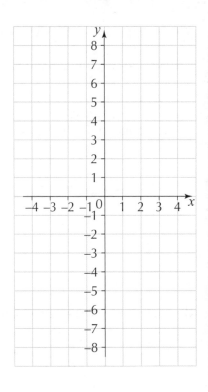

4 Some of these lines cross the y-axis at (0, 3). Circle them.

$y = x + 3$ $y = 3x$ $y = 3 - x$ $y = x - 3$ $y = 3 + 2x$

5 Match the equations to the lines on the graph by drawing lines from the letters to the equations.

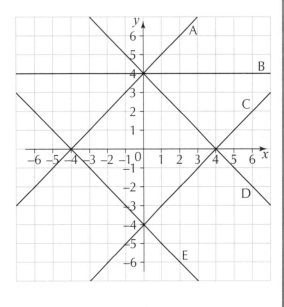

A •   • $y = 4$

B •   • $y = 4 + x$

C •   • $y = 4 - x$

D •   • $y = x - 4$

E •   • $y = -4 - x$

> **Exam hint**
>
> You can start with the equations or the graph. Eliminate the easiest ones first.

6 Here are the equations of some straight lines. Circle those that pass through the point (10, 15).

$y = 10$ $y = 15$ $y = x + 5$ $y = 2x + 5$

$y = 2x - 5$ $y = 3x - 15$ $y = 25 - x$ $y = 30 - 2x$

7 The equation of line A is $y = 2x$.

Write down the equations of lines B and C.

The equation of line B is ....

The equation of line C is ....

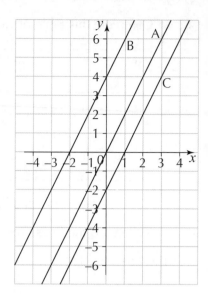

8 Match the parallel lines. One has been done for you.

$y = 2 - x$ •   • $y = 4 - 4x$

$y = 2 + x$ •   • $y = x - 4$

$y = 2x + 4$ •   • $y = 2x + 2$

$y = 2 - 4x$ •   • $y = 4x + 4$

$y = 4x + 2$ •   • $y = 4 - 2x$

$y = 2 - 2x$ •   • $y = 4 - x$

9 Look at the six lettered lines on this graph.

Write the correct letter next to each equation.

a $y = \frac{1}{2}x$ ....

b $y = 2x$ ....

c $y = -x$ ....

d $y = -\frac{1}{2}x$ ....

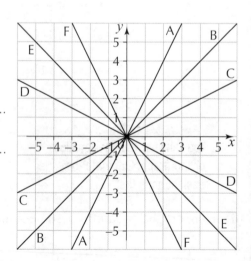

10 Write down the equation of the straight line through the points.

a (2, 0), (4, 2), (6, 4) and (0, −2) ....

b (0, 0), (2, 10), (5, 25) and (−2, −10) ....

c (0,10), (4, 14), (8, 18), (−10, 0) ....

11 Here are the equations of three lines. Each line passes through several of the points on the diagram.

Identify the points on each line.

a $y = 2x + 2$

....

....

....

b $y = 5 - x$

....

....

....

c $y = x - 1$

....

....

....

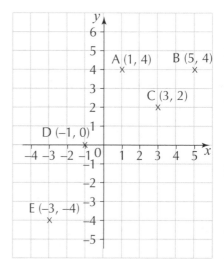

12 Find the equation of this straight line.

....

....

....

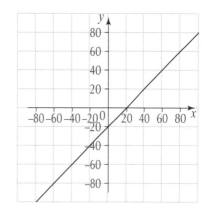

Real-life graphs

In this section you will:
- interpret graphs arising from real-life situations
- construct functions arising from real-life problems and plot their corresponding graphs.

5

1 A company uses this method to work out its fees.

cost of taxi hire = fixed charge of £4 + £2 per kilometre travelled

a Write this formula in symbols.

Use C for the cost (in pounds) and D for the number of kilometres travelled.

....

b Find the cost of a taxi ride of 32 kilometres.

.... £...............

2 When he went on holiday, Howard used this graph to change prices in pounds into euros.

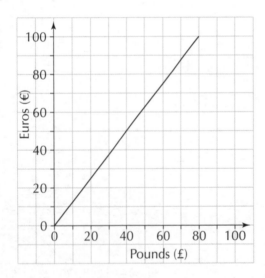

a How many euros are equivalent to £50?

£50 ≈ € ....

b A ticket to a show cost Howard 40 euros. How many pounds is that? ....

c On his way home on the ferry, Howard saw a watch priced at £60. Howard had €80 left. Could he afford to buy the watch? Explain how you decided.

....

....

3 Al walks to the shop and back.
This graph shows his journey.

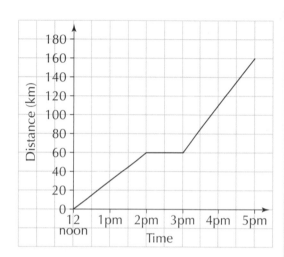

a How far did Al walk to the shop?

.... m

b How long did it take to get there?

.... minutes

c How long did he stay at the shop? .... minutes

d How long did Al take to walk home? .... minutes

4 This graph shows a car journey.

a How far did the car travel in the first hour?

.... km

b What happened at 2pm?

....

c How far did the car travel between 3pm and 5pm?

.... km

5 A walker starts to walk.

20 minutes later a cyclist starts from the same place in the same direction.

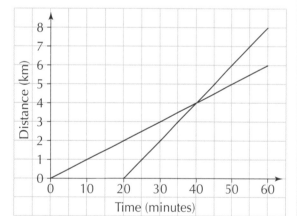

a How long does it take the walker to walk 3 kilometres?

.... minutes

b How far has the cyclist travelled when she passes the walker?

.... km

c When the walker has been walking for an hour, how far ahead of him is the cyclist?

.... km

6 The cost of hiring a bike from Bike4U is a fixed charge of £5 plus £1 per hour.

a Write down a formula for the cost C, in pounds of hire for T hours.

....

b Draw a graph to show the cost for hiring a bike from Bike4U for up to 8 hours

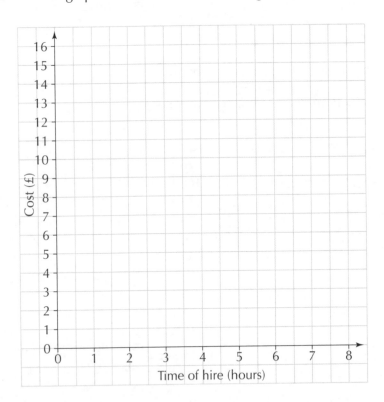

c Wheelers have no fixed charge but the cost of hiring
a bike from them is £2 per hour.

On the same graph as you used for part **b**, draw a line to show their charges.

d A friend asks you which is cheaper, Bike4U or Wheelers.

What would you say?

....

....

....

....

7 Mobile phone Tariff A costs £10 per month for up to 100 texts and then 5p per text after that. This is shown on the graph.

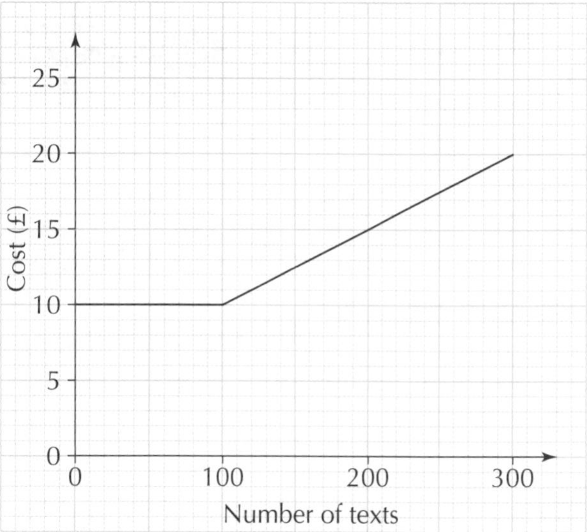

  a Tariff B is £5 for up to 100 texts and then 10p per text after that. Show this on the graph.

  b The salesperson says: 'Tariff B is cheaper than Tariff A.' Is this true? Write a more precise comparison of the cost of each tariff.

    ....

    ....

    ....

    ....

Exam hint

The point where the lines cross is important.

8 A car driver leaves home at 9am. This graph shows his journey.

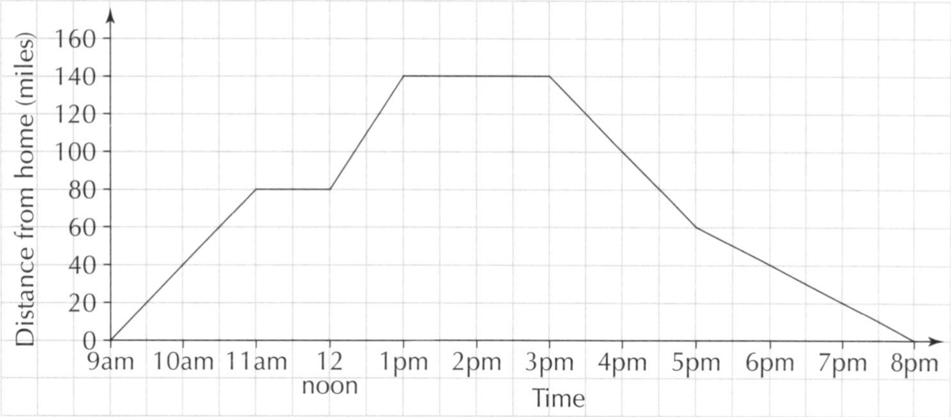

  a At what time is the driver 60 miles from home?

    ....

  b The driver stops for a break twice.

    Between what times is the second break?

    between .... and ....

  c At what time does the driver start to return home?   ....

  d How long does the driver take on the return journey?   .... hours

  e Between what times is the car travelling fastest?

    ....

    .... between .... and ....

1 The nth term of a sequence is $3(2n + 5)$.

a 93 is a term in this sequence. Use this fact to write down an equation for n.

....

b Solve the equation. ....

.... $n =$ ....

2 Sara said: 'In 10 years' time my age will be the square of my age 10 years ago.'

a Sara is A years old. Use the information above to write down an equation involving A.

....

b Use trial and improvement to work out Sara's age.

....

....

.... years

3 The length of a rectangle is 1 cm greater than the width. The area is 99.75 cm^2.
Work out the width.

....

....

....

.... width = ... cm

4 Merry is solving an equation. He has made some errors.

$$6x - 10 = 2x + 18$$

Add $2x$ to both sides $8x - 10 = 18$

Subtract 10 from both sides $8x = 8$

Multiply by 8 $x = 64$

Write a correct version for Merry.

....

....

....

....

5 This graph shows the line $y = 2x - 4$.

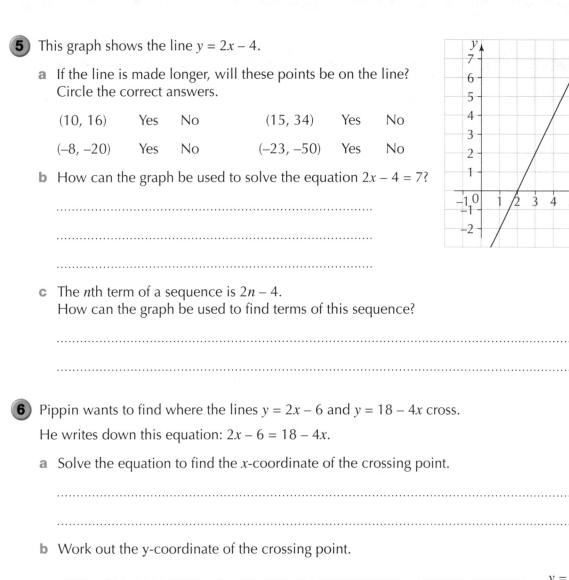

a If the line is made longer, will these points be on the line?
Circle the correct answers.

(10, 16)	Yes	No		(15, 34)	Yes	No
(−8, −20)	Yes	No		(−23, −50)	Yes	No

b How can the graph be used to solve the equation $2x - 4 = 7$?

....

....

....

c The nth term of a sequence is $2n - 4$.
How can the graph be used to find terms of this sequence?

....

....

6 Pippin wants to find where the lines $y = 2x - 6$ and $y = 18 - 4x$ cross.

He writes down this equation: $2x - 6 = 18 - 4x$.

a Solve the equation to find the x-coordinate of the crossing point.

....

....

b Work out the y-coordinate of the crossing point.

.... $y = ...$

7 Aaron starts jogging round a track. This chart shows
how far he travels in the first ten seconds.

a How can you tell from the chart that he jogged
faster in the first 5 seconds?

....

....

....

b If Aaron continues at the same rate after the
first 5 seconds, how far will he travel in 20 seconds?

....

.... metres

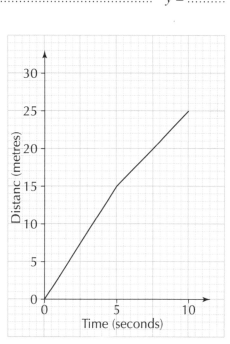

Shape, space and measure

11 Quadrilaterals

In this section you will classify quadrilaterals by their geometric properties.

5 **1** Draw all the lines of symmetry for each of these shapes.

a an equilateral triangle

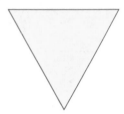

b an isosceles triangle

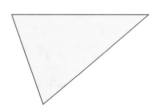

2 Write down the order of rotational symmetry of these shapes.

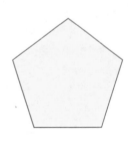

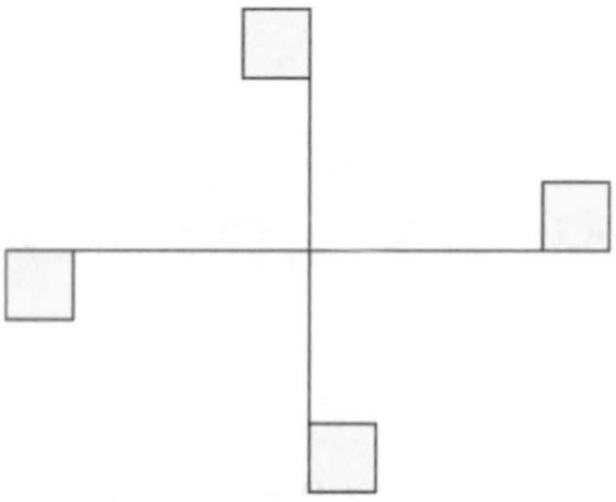

a order = ...

b order = ...

6 **3** Draw lines, from the names of the shapes in the left-hand column to the numbers in the right, to show the number of lines of symmetry of each shape.

Shape			**Number of lines of symmetry**
Kite	•	•	0
Parallelogram	•	•	1
Rectangle	•	•	2
Rhombus	•	•	3
Square	•	•	4

4 This delta (or arrowhead) has a line of symmetry.

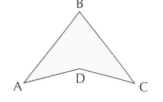

   a Which sides must be equal in length?

     ....

   b Which angles must be equal in size?

     ....

5 A trapezium can have a line of symmetry.

   a Draw a trapezium with a line of symmetry.

   b Mark the sides that must be equal.

   c Mark the angles that must be equal.

6 Draw lines, from the names of the shapes in the left-hand column to the numbers in the right, to show the order of rotational symmetry of each shape.

Shape	Order of rotational symmetry
Kite •	
	• 1
Parallelogram •	
	• 2
Rectangle •	
	• 3
Rhombus •	
	• 4
Square •	

7 Look at the shapes below.

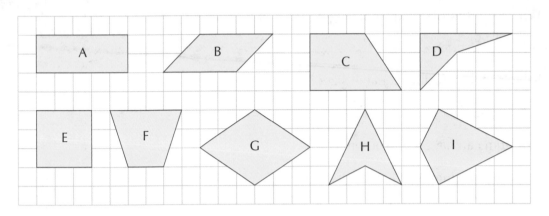

Write the letter of each shape in the correct box.

No angles equal	One pair of equal angles	Two pairs of equal angles	Four equal angles

8 Look again at the shapes in question **7**. Write the letter of each shape in the correct box.

No sides equal	One pair of equal sides	Two pairs of equal sides	Four equal sides

9 Two sides of a quadrilateral are 10 cm long and the other two are 15 cm long.

a Say whether the following statements **'Could be true'** or **'Must be false'**.

The shape is:

i a rectangle .... **ii** a kite ....

iii a parallelogram .... **iv** a rhombus ....

v a trapezium ....

b Justify your answer to the last statement about a trapezium.

....

....

12 Angles

In this section you will solve geometrical problems, using properties of angles, of parallel and intersecting lines, and of triangles and polygons.

1 Work out the size of each of the lettered angles in these diagrams.

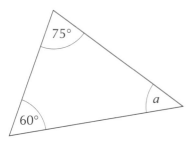

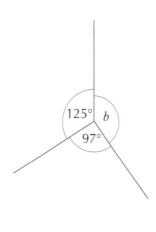

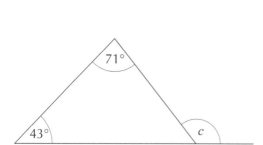

....

....

$a =$ .... $b =$ .... $c =$ ....

2 **a** The largest angle of an isosceles triangle is 124°.

Find the sizes of the other two angles.

....

....

.... and ....

b One angle of an isosceles triangle is 50°.

What could the other angles be?

....

....

3 Work out the value of x.

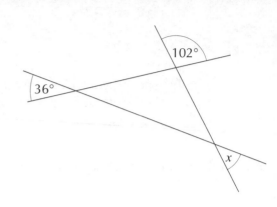

....

....

.... $x =$ ....

4 **a** Three angles of a quadrilateral are 75°.

Calculate the fourth angle.

....

.... 4th angle = ...

b Draw a sketch to show that the quadrilateral could be a kite.

5 ABCDEF is a regular hexagon.

a What type of quadrilateral is ABCD? ....

b Work out the angles of quadrilateral ABCD.

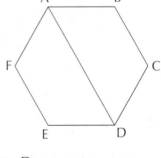

....

....

A: .... B: .... C: .... D: ....

6 The diagram shows two overlapping squares of the same size that have a common corner at A.

a Show that ABCD is a kite.

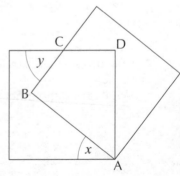

....

....

b The angle labelled x is 40°. Find the size of the angle labelled y.

....

....$y =$ ....

7 ABCDE is a regular pentagon. Each angle of a regular pentagon is 108°. Work out the angles of triangle ACD.

> **Exam hint**
> In questions like this ask yourself: 'What angles do I know? What angles can I work out?'

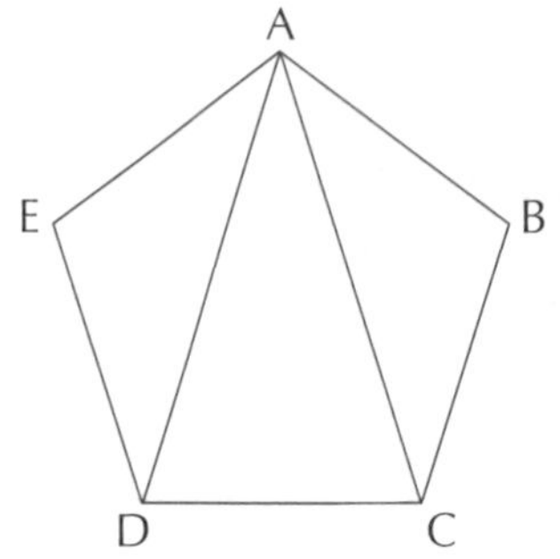

....

....

....

....

....

A: ....

C: ....

D: ....

8 The exterior angle of a regular polygon is 40°.
How many sides does it have?

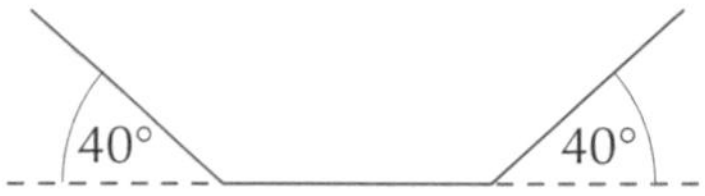

....

....

....

.... sides

9 This diagram shows a square and two equilateral triangles.
AB and BC are two sides of a regular polygon.

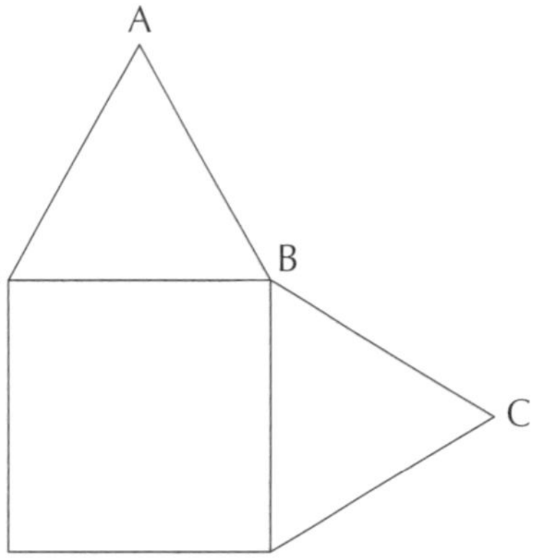

a How big is each angle of the regular polygon?

....

angle = ...

....

b How many sides does the polygon have?

....

....

....

.... sides

⑬ Geometric proof

In this section you will:
- identify alternate and corresponding angles
- understand a proof that the sum of the angles of a triangle is 180° and of a quadrilateral is 360°.

⑤

① Explain why the fourth angle of this trapezium must be 55°.

....

....

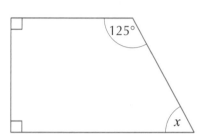

⑥

② Complete these sentences.

c and .... are opposite angles.

c and .... are corresponding angles.

c and .... are alternate angles.

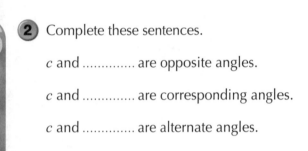

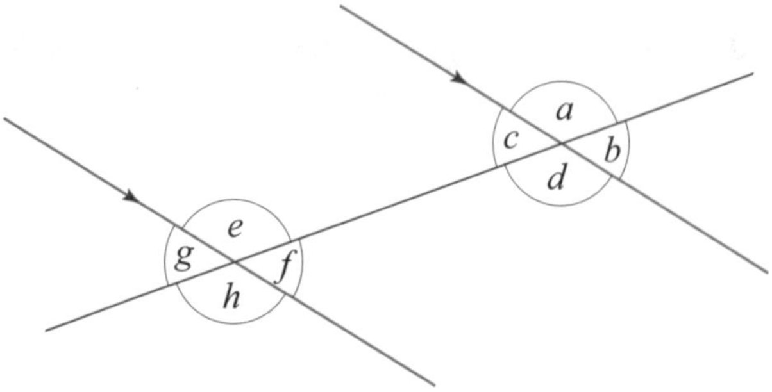

③ The capital letter Z has two alternate angles.

   a What other capital letter has two alternate angles? ....

   b What capital letter has two pairs of opposite angles? ....

④ Calculate the sizes of the lettered angles. Give a reason in each case.

a = ...

Reason: ....

b = ...

Reason: ....

c = ...

Reason: ....

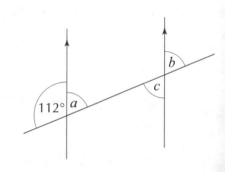

5 Calculate the angles of triangle ABC.
Give reasons for your answers.

A: ....

Reason: ....

B: ....

Reason: ....

C: ....

Reason: ....

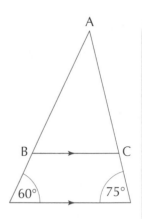

6 **a** Give a reason why $x = a$.

....

b Give a reason why $y = b$.

....

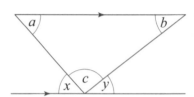

7 There are three pairs of parallel lines in this diagram.
Work out the sizes of the lettered angles.

$a = $ ....

$b = $ ....

$c = $ ....

$d = $ ....

$e = $ ....

$f = $ ....

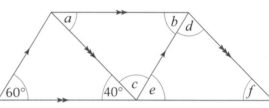

Exam hint

You can work them out in any
order. Do the easy ones first.

8 **a** What is the value of $a + b + f$?

....

b Use the two triangles to explain why the angles of this
quadrilateral must add up to 360°.

....

....

....

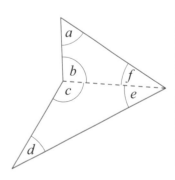

9 Tristan wrote:

The quadrilateral is divided into four triangles.

The angles of each triangle add up to 180°.

The total of all the angles of the triangles is 4 × 180° = 720°.

The angles of the quadrilateral are the same as the angles of the triangles, so the angles of the quadrilateral add up to 720°.

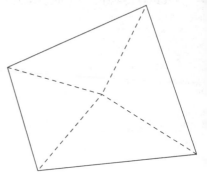

a What mistake has Tristan made?

....

b Modify Tristan's proof to make it correct.

....

....

....

....

....

10 ABCD is a trapezium.

    a Explain why $a = e$.

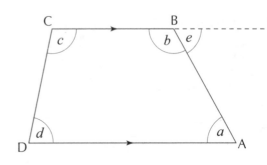

....

....

    b Explain why $a + b = 180°$.

....

....

    c Explain why $c + d = 180°$.

....

....

14 Three dimensions

In this section you will visualise and use 2-D representations of 3-D objects.

1 A cube has:

.... faces

.... vertices (corners)

.... edges

2 This is the net of a cube.

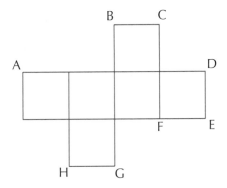

Which other lettered points will meet at point A to form a vertex of the cube?

....

3 There is a stack of three cubes standing on a table.

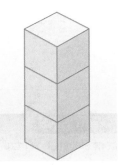

How many cube faces are visible altogether, without lifting any cubes?

....

4 This diagram shows a shape made from four cubes.

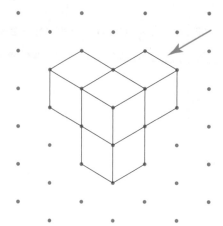

Draw the view from the direction shown.

5 This is the front elevation of an object.

Which of these could it be?

Circle the possible shapes.

CYLINDER   SPHERE   CUBOID

CUBE   PRISM

Exam hint
front elevation = front view

6 This is a cuboid with two corners removed.

a How many faces does it have?

....

b How many edges does it have?

....

7 This is a triangular prism made of wood.

The cross-section is an equilateral triangle.

Isolde wants to cut it in half so that the two pieces are identical. How many ways are there to do that?

.... ways

8 This is the net of a 3-D shape.

a How many faces will it have?

....

b How many edges will it have?

....

c How many vertices will it have?

....

d Two faces of the net will be opposite one another.

Shade them on the net.

6

9 This is the front view of a shape made from cubes.
Which of the diagrams below could be a plan view?
Circle the possible answers.

Exam hint

plan view = overhead view

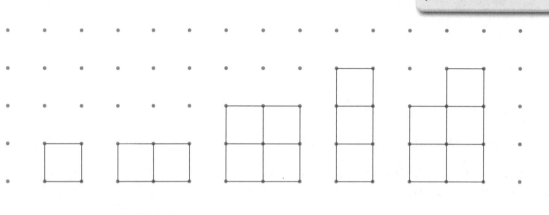

10 This is the net of a pyramid with a square base.

a Which side will join to side *a* to make an edge?

....

b If the pyramid stands on its square base, draw a plan view.

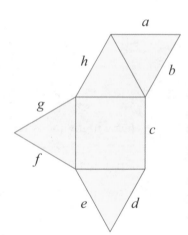

⑮ Enlargement

In this section you will enlarge 2-D shapes, given a centre of enlargement and a positive whole-number scale factor.

① On the grid on the right, draw a shape similar to this but with all the sides twice as long.

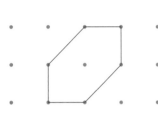

② **a** Draw the triangle with vertices at (2, 1), (2, 4) and (4, 1).

b Now draw the triangle with vertices at (4, 2), (4, 8) and (8, 2).

c What can you say about the angles of the two triangles?

....

....

....

d What can you say about the sides of the two triangles?

....

....

....

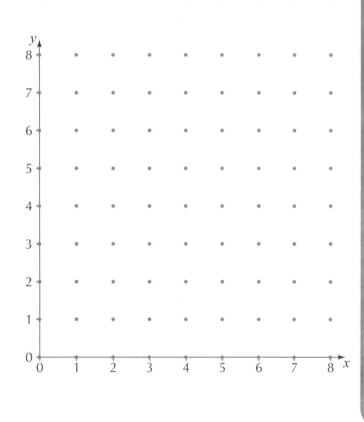

6

3 Enlarge this shape with a scale factor of 4.

The centre of enlargement is marked with a cross.

4 **a** Enlarge this shape with a scale factor of 3.

The centre of enlargement is marked with a cross.

b The perimeter of the original shape is 8 units.

What is the perimeter of the enlargement?

....

....

....

c Penny said: 'When you enlarge a shape with a scale factor of 3, the perimeter will be three times bigger.'

Explain why this is the case.

....

....

....

....

5 **a** Draw an enlargement of the triangle, centre X, scale factor 2.

b The original shape is 3 units long and 2 units high.

What are the length and height of the enlargement?

length = ...   height = ...

c Julia wrote: 'The original triangle has an area of 3 squares. An enlargement of scale factor 2 will have an area of 3 × 2 = 6 squares.'

Is this correct? If not, what is the area of the enlargement?

....

....

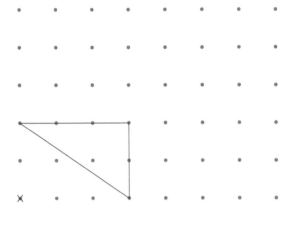

6 Triangle T is enlarged to give triangle E.

a Mark the centre of enlargement with a cross.

b What is the scale factor? ....

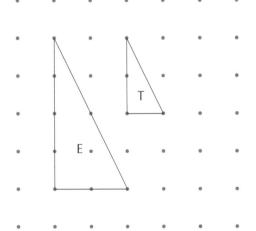

7 Marcus has started to enlarge the shape ABCD.
A'B' is the image of AB.

    a Complete the enlargement.

    b What is the scale factor? ....

    c Mark the centre of the enlargement
    with a cross.

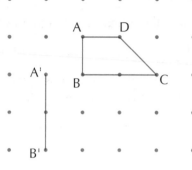

8 Explain why triangle B cannot be an enlargement of
triangle A.

....

....

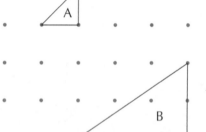

9 A shape is enlarged with a scale factor of 5.

    a One side on the enlargement is 6 centimetres long.

    How long is the corresponding side on the original shape?

    .... length = ... cm

    b An angle on the enlargement is 150°.

    How large is the corresponding angle on the original shape?

    .... angle = ...

16 Congruence

In this section you will use the fact that translations, rotations and reflections preserve length and angle and map objects onto congruent images.

1 State whether each shape is a reflection, rotation or translation of the shaded triangle T.

A ....   B ....

C ....   D ....

E ....

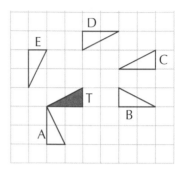

2 Draw the image of the triangle after a 90° clockwise rotation about vertex A.

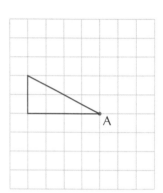

3 Which shapes are congruent to A?

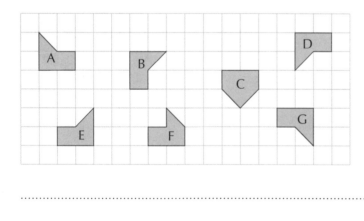

....

....

Exam hint

Ask for tracing paper if it helps you.

4 B is a reflection of A.

a Draw the mirror line on the diagram.

b Mark the images of X and Y and label them X′ and Y′.

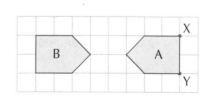

5 B is the image of A after a rotation of 180°.

   a Mark the centre of rotation.

   b Mark the images of X and Z and label them X′ and Z′.

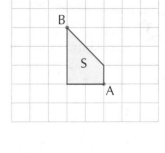

6 **a** Rotate shape S through 90° clockwise about vertex A.
Label the image T.

   b Rotate shape S through 90° clockwise about vertex B.
Label the image U.

   c Which of these transformations will map T onto U?
Circle your answer.

   REFLECTION   ROTATION   TRANSLATION

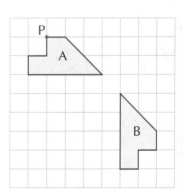

7 B is the image of A after a reflection.

   a Mark the image of vertex P and label it P′.

   b One angle of A is 45°.
Mark the image of this angle on B.

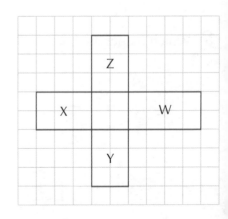

8 W, X, Y and Z are four rectangles.

   a Say whether Y could be the image of X after:

      i a reflection ....   **ii** a rotation ....

      iii a translation. ....

   b Explain why W cannot be the image of X after a
reflection, a rotation or a translation.

     ....

     ....

9 Could Y be the image of X after:

   a a translation   ....

   b a translation followed by a reflection ....

   c a reflection followed by a translation ....

   d two translations   ....

   e two reflections?   ....

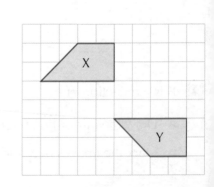

17 Constructions

In this section you will use a straight edge and compasses to do standard constructions.

1 Measure the three angles and the longest side of this triangle.

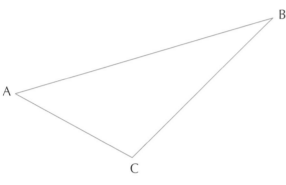

A: ....

B: ....

C: ....

longest side = ...

2 Draw a triangle with sides 6.5 cm, 5.7 cm and 4.2 cm.
One side has been drawn for you.

6.5 cm

3 **a** Draw this triangle accurately in the space below.

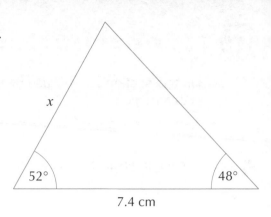

x

52°

48°

7.4 cm

b On your triangle, measure the side marked x in the sketch above. $x =$ .... cm

4 **a** Draw a perpendicular line from C to AD. Leave your construction lines on the diagram.

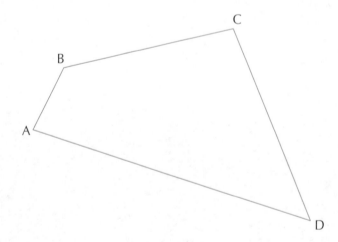

C

B

A

D

b Draw the bisector of angle D.

c The lines you have drawn in parts **a** and **b** cross at P.

Measure the length of CP.   CP = ... cm

5 a Use a straight edge and compasses to draw the perpendicular bisectors of AB and AC. Leave your construction lines on the diagram.

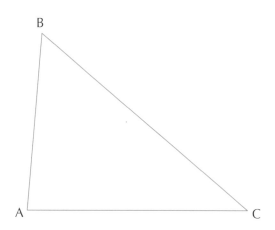

b The lines you drew in part **a** meet at Z. Measure the distance from Z to each vertex of the triangle.

ZA = ... cm   ZB = ... cm   ZC = ... cm

6 a Use a straight edge and compasses to draw the bisector of each angle of this triangle.

b What can you say about the places where the lines cross one another?

....

....

7 **a** Use a straight edge and compasses to draw
this kite accurately.

Leave your construction lines on your drawing.

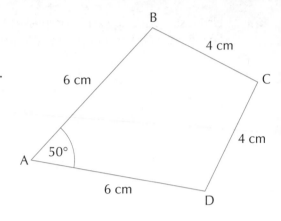

b Measure the lenth of AC.

AC = ... cm

18 Area and volume

In this section you will:
- deduce and use formulae for the area of a triangle and parallelogram, and the volume of a cuboid
- calculate the volumes and surface areas of cuboids.

1

12 cm	8 cm	10 cm	8 cm

2 cm | A | 3 cm | B | 4 cm | C | 5 cm | D |

a Which rectangles have the same area? ....

....

b Which rectangles have the same perimeter? ....

....

2 Which of these calculations can you use to work out the area of the triangle?

4 cm   3 cm

5 cm

Circle the correct one.

$\frac{3 \times 4}{2}$ $\frac{4 \times 5}{2}$ $\frac{5 \times 3}{2}$ $\frac{4 \times 5}{2}$ None of these

3 Work out the area of each shape.

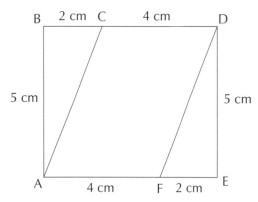

B   2 cm   C   4 cm   D

5 cm   5 cm

A   4 cm   F   2 cm   E

a rectangle ABDE ....

....

.... cm²

b triangle ABC ....

....

.... cm²

c parallelogram ACDF ....

....

.... cm²

6

4 ACDE is a rectangle.
Find the area of each shape.

a triangle ABE ....

....

.... cm²

b triangle EBD ....

....

.... cm²

5 The area of this triangle is 30 cm². Work out the value of *a*.

....

....

.... *a* = ...

6 Calculate the area of the
shaded region of this rectangle.

....

.... area = ... cm²

7 Work out the area of this parallelogram.

....

....

....

....

.... area = ... cm²

8 The sides of a right-angled triangle are 8 m, 15 m and 17 m.
Work out the area of the triangle.

....

....

....

.... area = ... m²

9 a Calculate the volume of this cuboid.

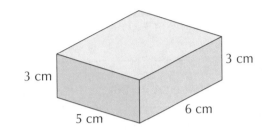

....

.... volume = ... cm³

b Calculate the surface area of the cuboid.

....

.... surface area = ... cm²

10 A box without a lid is made from cardboard.
The base is a square of side 12 cm.
The box is 4 cm high.

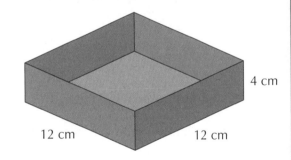

a What is the total area of cardboard used to make the box?

....

.... area = ... cm²

b Work out the volume of the box.

....

.... volume = ... cm³

c A box with the same volume has a square base of side 8 cm.
How high is it?

.... height = ... cm

⑲ Circles

> In this section you will know and use the formulae for the circumference and area of a circle.

5

1 An approximate formula for the area, A, of a circle of radius r cm is $A = 3r^2$.
Use this formula to find the value of:

   a A when $r = 4$ ....

   .... $A =$ .... cm

   b r when $A = 108$ ....

   .... $r =$ ....cm

6

2 The diameter of a discus circle is 2.5 metres.

   a   Work out the circumference of the discus circle.

   ....

   .... m

   b   Work out the area of the discus circle.

   ....

   .... m^2

2.5 m

3 The radius of a circle is 5.0 cm.

   a   Work out the circumference, in centimetres, to the nearest millimetre.

   ....

   .... circumference = ... cm

   b   Work out the area to an appropriate degree of accuracy.

   ....

   .... area = ... cm^2

> **Exam hint**
> The appropriate accuracy depends on the initial value of 5.0.

4 A trundle wheel is used to measure distances. It has a wheel that has a circumference of exactly 1 metre.

   a Work out the diameter of the wheel, to the nearest millimetre.

   ....

   .... cm

   b Work out the area of one side of the wheel.

   ....

   .... cm^2

5 The diameter of a bicycle wheel is 68 cm. How many complete revolutions will the wheel make if the bicycle travels 100 metres?

....

.... revolutions

6 The diameter of a 2p coin is 26 mm.

   a How long is the edge of a 2p coin?

   .... length = ... mm

   b Work out the area of one face of the coin.

   ....

   .... area = ... mm^2

7 This is a quarter of a circle of radius 15 cm.

   Work out:

   15 cm

   a the area ....

   ....

   .... area = ... cm^2

   b the perimeter. ....

   ....

   .... perimeter = ... cm

8 The diagram shows two circles. The diameters of the circles are 8 cm and 16 cm.

Work out the area between the two circles.

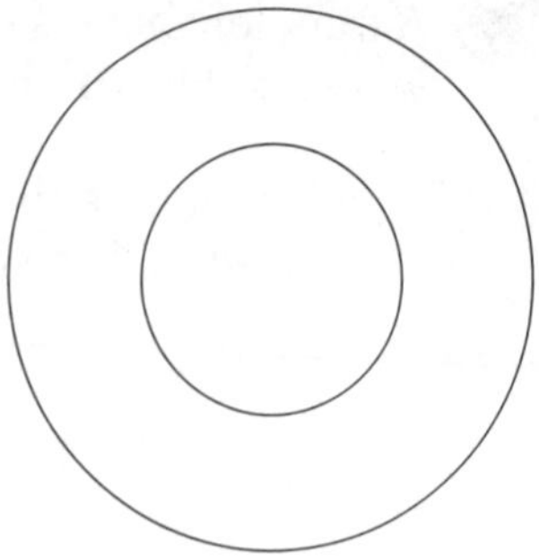

....

....

....

.... cm^2

9 **a** Work out the area of the shaded section.

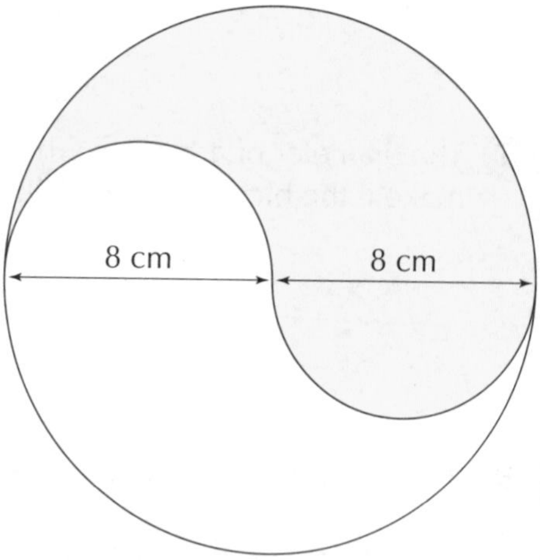

....

....

....

.... area = ... cm^2

b Work out the perimeter of the shaded section.

....

....

....

.... perimeter = ... cm

10 This diagram shows a 400 metre running track. There are two 90 m straights and a semi-circular curve at each end.

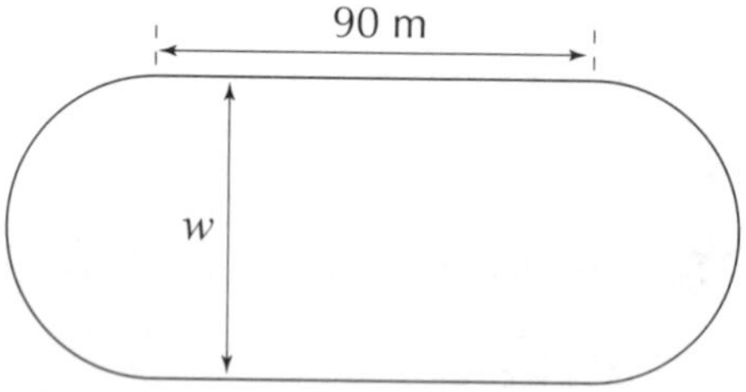

a Work out the width, w.

....

....

.... w = ... m

b Work out the area inside the track.

....

....

.... area = ... m^2

1 **a** Construct a perpendicular from C to AB.

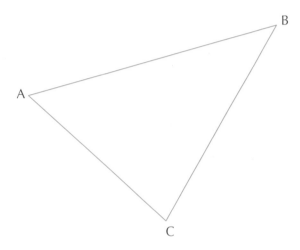

b By taking suitable measurements, work out the area of the triangle. Show your calculations.

....

....

.... area = ... cm²

2 This is the net of a cuboid. All the dimensions are in centimetres. Work out:

a the surface area of the cuboid ....

....

.... surface area = ... cm²

b the volume of the cuboid. ....

....

.... volume = ... cm³

3 The volume of a cuboid is 60 cm³. All the sides are whole numbers of centimetres. All the sides are longer than one centimetre.

List the lengths of the sides of two possible cuboids.

....

First possibility   ....

Second possibility   ....

4 Three congruent rhombuses fit together to make a regular hexagon.

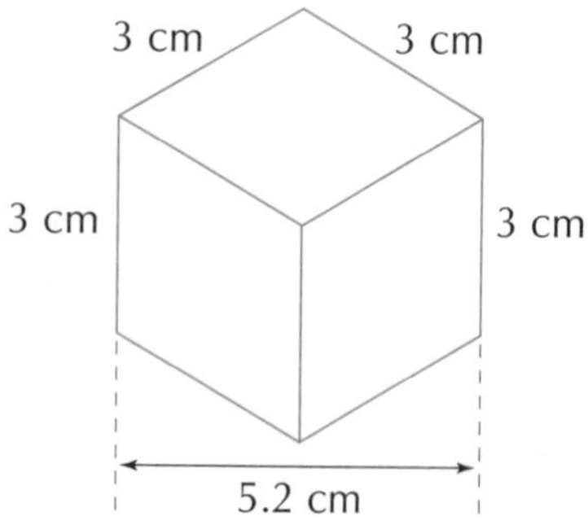

a Work out the angles of each rhombus.

....

....

.... Angles are ....

3 cm   3 cm

3 cm   3 cm

5.2 cm

b Work out the area of the hexagon.

....

....

.... area = ... cm²

5 The diagram shows a circle touching two squares.

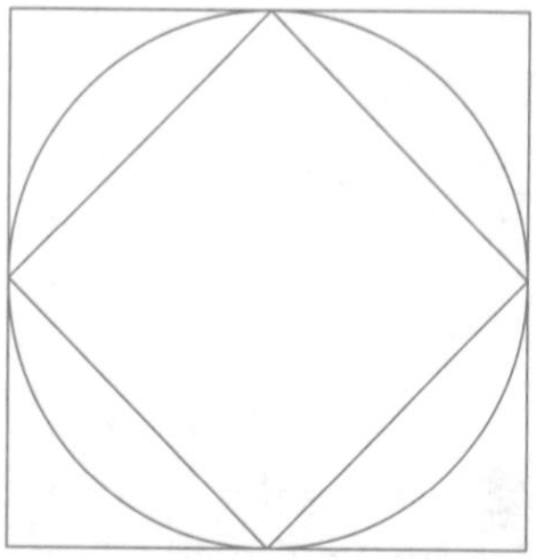

The area of the outside square is 100 cm².

a Work out the area of the circle.

....

....

....

.... area = ... cm²

b Work out the area of the inside square.

....

....

....

.... area = ... cm²

6 Angle ABC = 53°. Work out:

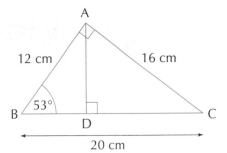

 a angle CAD ....

....

.... angle = ...°

 b the area of triangle ABC ....

....

.... area = ... cm²

 c the length of AD. ....

....

.... AD = ... cm

7 This is part of a tessellation of squares and regular octagons.

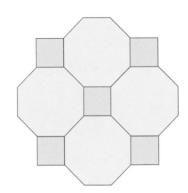

 a Explain how the diagram can be used to show that each angle of a regular octagon is 135°.

....

....

 b Explain why it is not possible to make a tessellation out of equilateral triangles and regular pentagons.

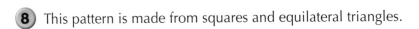

8 This pattern is made from squares and equilateral triangles.

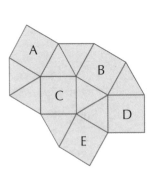

 a Square A can be rotated about one corner onto square C.

 What is the angle of rotation?

.... angle = ...

 b Onto which squares can square A be translated? ....

 c Square A can be reflected onto square C.

 Draw the mirror line on the pattern.

Handling data

⑳ Surveys

In this section you will:
- design a survey or experiment
- design data-collection sheets
- design tables, choosing suitable class intervals
- design and use two-way tables.

5

1 Jasmine wants to find out how many cars the families in her street own. She decides to count the cars on the drive or outside each house.

    a Give three reasons why this method could give incorrect data.

       1 ....

       2 ....

       3 ....

    b Suggest a better method of collecting the data.

       ....

6

2 A data-collection sheet for the heights of seedlings has these class intervals.

    a What problems might arise with these intervals?

Height (cm)	Frequency
1–5	
5–10	
10–15	
15–20	

       ....

       ....

       ....

    b Suggest class intervals that will overcome these problems.

       ....

3 Alice is carrying out a survey. She wants to find out if people would like a cinema in the town where she lives. She wants to get opinions from a wide range of people. She will ask people:

- outside the local primary school
- outside the supermarket
- outside the sports centre.

a Name one group of people who might **not** be included in her survey.

....

b Suggest one other place that will help her to get a broader range of replies.

....

4 This two-way table shows the result of an experiment to see how long children took to carry out a simple task.

	Less than 1 minute	1 to 2 minutes	More than 2 minutes
Boys	40	150	60
Girls	80	100	20

a How many girls were involved? ....

b How many children took 1 to 2 minutes? ....

c Who were quicker at the task, boys or girls? Give a reason for your answer.

....

....

5 Liz asks people how they will vote in a general election. She wants to divide the results into about six different age groups for analysis. Suggest age groups she could use. Give a brief reason for your choice.

....

....

6 Here are the genders and times for 20 participants in a sponsored run. (M = male and F = female; times are in minutes.)

M 32, F 38, M 39, M 39, M 40, F 41, M 41, M 41, M 45, M 47

F 48, F 52, F 53, F 53, F 55, F 55, M 55, M 58, M 62, F 64

Put the appropriate numbers in this two-way table.

Time (minutes)	30–39	40–49	50–59	60–69
Male				
Female				

7 Do older students spend more time doing homework than younger ones do? To answer this question, Ann has collected the following information from 200 students:

name, address, age, school year, maths teacher, number of brothers and sisters, hours spent on homework last week.

To answer her question she wants to record the number of people in different categories in a two-way table.

a What two categories should she use for the rows and columns?

....

b Suggest one other question Ann could answer with the data she has collected.

....

21 Representing data

In this section you will select, construct and modify pie charts, bar charts, frequency diagrams, time graphs and scatter diagrams and decide which are the most useful in the context of a problem.

1 This pie chart shows where a group of people went on a foreign holiday.

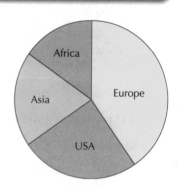

Find each of the following, if possible.

If it is not possible, say so.

a The least popular area ....

b The number who went to Europe ....

c The percentage who went to the USA ....

2 This bar chart shows the numbers of people travelling on three different buses, 1, 2 and 3.

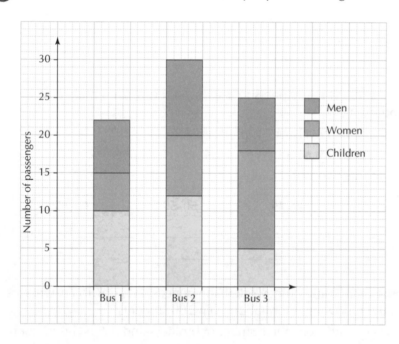

a How many men were on bus 1? ....

b Which bus had the most women?

Give a reason for your answer.

....

....

3 What type of chart is most appropriate to show the following data? Choose from:

pie chart   bar chart   time graph   scatter graph

a Votes for different parties in an election

Blue	Green	Red	Yellow	Other
2510	3405	1922	2350	150

....

b Ages of people in two countries

Millions	Under 18	18 – 60	Over 60
Utopia	16	42	14
Erewhon	10	35	19

....

c Unemployment rates

2007	2008	2009	2010	2011
7%	9%	10%	14%	12%

....

4 This table shows the percentages of boys and girls in three different schools.

	Percentage		
	School X	School Y	School Z
Boys	40	70	50
Girls	60	30	50

Show the information in a sectional bar chart.

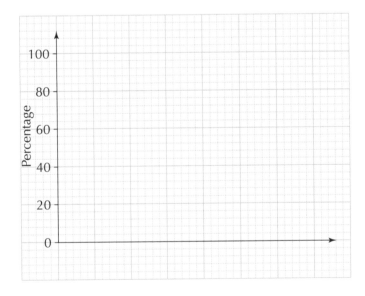

5 Here are the votes for four competitors in a contest. Show the information in a pie chart.

Competitor	A	B	C	D
Votes	60	200	150	40

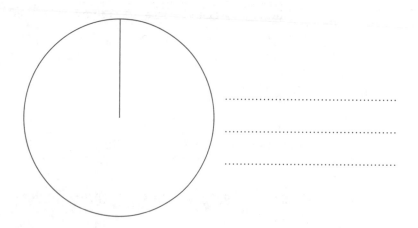

....

....

....

> **Exam hint**
>
> Show any calculations you do to work out angles.

6 This table shows the scores of ten people for a practical task and a reasoning task.

	Score									
	A	**B**	**C**	**D**	**E**	**F**	**G**	**H**	**I**	**J**
Practical	15	12	8	10	9	10	4	9	10	6
Reasoning	10	13	12	6	13	10	9	11	12	10

Show these results on a scatter diagram.

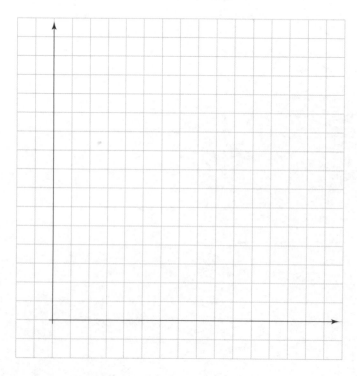

7 This table shows the percentages of students gaining five good GCSEs in two schools over six years.

	Percentage					
	2006	2007	2008	2009	2010	2011
Crofton High	70	70	65	60	54	62
Grove School	50	40	48	55	60	70

Show the data in a time chart.

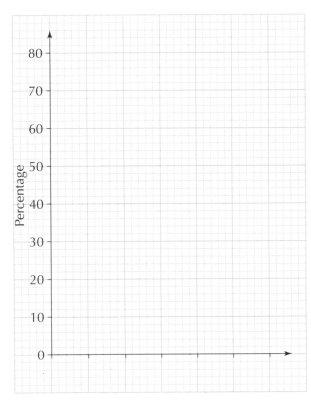

8 Alan and Betty each threw a dice 40 times. They recorded the frequencies of each score.

	Score					
	1	2	3	4	5	6
Alan	5	10	8	6	8	3
Betty	7	4	10	8	6	5

Show these results in a suitable diagram.

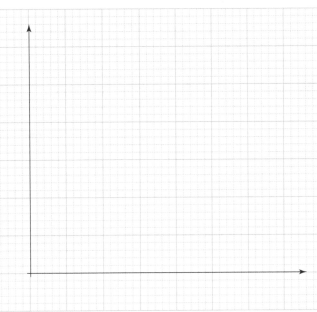

22 Outcomes

In this section you will find and record all possible mutually exclusive outcomes for single events and two successive events in a systematic way.

1 Balls numbered from 1 to 50 are put in a box. One ball is taken out. Write down the probability that the number on the ball:

a ends with a 0 .... **b** is 20 or less ....

c is an even number .... **d** is a multiple of 4. ....

2 In a class of 20 students, 13 are boys. Three of the boys and four of the girls wear glasses. A student is chosen at random. What is the probability that the student:

a is a girl .... **b** wears glasses .... **c** is a girl with glasses? ....

3 A dice is thrown and the number is squared.

a List all the possible outcomes.

....

b What is the probability that the outcome is more than 20? ....

4 Four cards, numbered 1, 2, 3 and 4, are placed face down on a table. Two of the cards are turned over at random.

a List all the possible pairs of cards. ....

....

b What is the probability that the numbers 1 and 2 are turned over? ....

c What is the probability that 4 is one of the cards? ....

d What is the probability that one card is even and the other is odd? ....

5 Two spinners each have four equal sections, numbered 1 to 4. Each is spun and the numbers are added.

a Show the possible totals on a sample space diagram.

b How many different possible totals are there? ....

c Find the probability that the total is:

i 8 .... **ii** 3 .... **iii** 5 ....

6 Two coins are tossed. Tom says there are three equally likely outcomes, two heads, two tails and one of each. Jerry says that is not correct and there are four equally likely outcomes. Explain why Jerry is correct.

....

....

....

7 Two dice are thrown and the scores are multiplied together.

Exam hint

The result of a multiplication is called a product.

a Show all the possible products on the outcome space diagram.

b What is the probability that the product is:

i 2 .... **ii** 30 or more? ....

8 **a** A coin is tossed and a dice is thrown. List all the possible outcomes.

....

....

b What is the probability of a head and an even number? ....

9 One set of three cards has the letters A, B and C. A second set of three cards has the letters X, Y and Z. One card is taken at random from each set.

a List all the possible outcomes.

....

....

b Find the probability that:

i the cards B and Y are chosen .... **ii** A is chosen but X is not ....

iii neither C nor Z is chosen. ....

(23) Probability

In this section you will know that the sum of probabilities of all mutually exclusive outcomes is one, and use this when solving problems.

1 A teacher recorded the numbers of students absent from each of her 25 classes in one week.

Number of absentees	0	1	2	3	4
Number of classes	8	6	5	1	5

Use this table to estimate the probability that in one lesson the number of absent students will be:

a 0 ....

b 1 or 2 ....

c more than 2 ....

This table shows the results for a second week.

Number of absentees	0	1	2	3	4
Number of classes	4	4	8	6	3

d Use the data in both tables to make a revised estimate of the probability that there will be no absentees in a lesson. Give your answer as a percentage.

.... probability = ...%

2 Each day the weather can be wet, cloudy or sunny. The probability that tomorrow will be wet is 0.3 and the probability that it will be cloudy is 0.1. Find the probability that tomorrow will be:

a wet or cloudy ....

b sunny ....

c not wet. ....

3 In a survey of vehicles using a busy road, 65% were cars, 10% were vans, 5% were motorbikes and the rest were lorries. Find the probability that a vehicle is:

a not a motorbike ....

b not a car ....

c a lorry. ....

4 A spinner can show one of four colours: red, blue, green or yellow. Green and yellow are equally likely. Complete this table of probabilities.

Colour	Red	Blue	Green	Yellow
Probability	0.4	0.3		

5 The probabilities of earthquakes in a particular country in a year are shown in this table.

Number of earthquakes	1	2	3	More than 3
Probability	20%	8%	3%	1%

Find the probability of:

a no earthquakes ....

b at least two earthquakes. ....

6 When two dice are thrown, the probability of two sixes is $\frac{1}{36}$ and the probability of just one six is $\frac{5}{18}$. Find the probability of:

   a not throwing two sixes .... **b** not throwing any sixes ....

   c throwing two fives .... **d** throwing just one five ....

   e not throwing any fives .... **f** not throwing any ones. ....

7 In a raffle, 50 tickets numbered from 1 to 50 are put in a box. There are two prizes, so two tickets are taken out of the box. Beth and her friends have bought 10 tickets.

   The probability that they win both prizes is 0.04.

   The probability that they win one prize is 0.33.

   Find the probability that they:

   a do not win both prizes .... **b** do not win any prizes. ....

8 A football manager thinks that his team's chance of winning the next match is 60% and the chance of losing is 5%. Find is probability that the team:

   a will not win .... **b** will not lose .... **c** will draw. ....

9 20% of cars on the road are less than 5 years old.

   35% are between 5 and 10 years old.

   30% are between 10 and 15 years old.

   What is the probability that a car is:

   a more than 5 years old .... **b** more than 10 years old ....

   c more than 15 years old? ....

10 Four coins are thrown.

   The probability of scoring 4 heads is $\frac{1}{16}$.

   The probability of scoring at least 3 heads is $\frac{5}{16}$.

   The probability of scoring at least 2 heads is $\frac{11}{16}$.

   Find the probability of scoring:

   a fewer than 4 heads .... **b** fewer than 2 heads ....

   c exactly 3 heads .... **d** exactly 2 heads. ....

11 When two coins are thrown, the probability of scoring no heads is $\frac{1}{4}$.

   When three coins are thrown, the probability of scoring no heads is $\frac{1}{8}$.

   When four coins are thrown, the probability of scoring no heads is $\frac{1}{16}$.

   Work out the probability that, when five coins are thrown, there will be at least one head. Explain how you find your answer.

   ....

   ....

㉔ Interpreting data

In this section you will communicate interpretations and results of a statistical survey, using tables, graphs and diagrams.

1 These two pie charts show information about the results of matches for a football team and a netball team.

The statements listed below may be true or false.

Which ones can you say are true or false on the basis of the information contained in the pie charts?

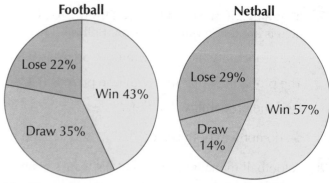

Answer True (T), False (F) or Cannot decide (C).

a The football team played more games than the netball team. ....

b The netball team won more games than it lost. ....

c The football team won more games than the netball team. ....

d The netball team drew a greater proportion of their games than the football team. ....

e Only girls play netball. ....

These tables show the average weekly alcohol consumption for men and women in Great Britain from 1998 to 2008. The numbers are units of alcohol.

Men	1998	2000	2002	2004	2006	2008
Beer	10.8	10.5	10.5	9.9	10.7	10.2
Spirits	2.2	2.1	2.1	2.0	2.0	2.1
Wine	2.4	2.5	2.9	2.6	3.0	5.2
Alcopops	0.2	0.2	0.7	0.5	0.3	0.3
Total	15.6	15.3	16.2	15.0	16.0	17.8

Women	1998	2000	2002	2004	2006	2008
Beer	2.0	2.4	1.7	1.9	1.6	1.3
Spirits	1.6	1.9	1.7	1.5	1.7	1.3
Wine	2.6	2.9	3.1	2.9	3.2	4.8
Alcopops	0.2	0.7	0.9	0.7	0.4	0.4
Total	6.4	7.9	7.4	7.0	6.9	7.8

Source: *www.statistics.gov.uk*

Question 2 and 3 show some statements based on the data in the tables. In each case you must decide on the best type of graph or chart to illustrate the statement, and draw it.

(2) 'Men drank more than twice as many units as women in 2008. Men drank a lot more beer. The amounts of wine and alcopops were similar.'

Draw a chart to compare the different quantities of each type drunk by men and women in 2008.

(3) 'The amount of wine drunk by both men and women has increased from 1998 to 2008.'

Draw a graph to show how the amount of wine drunk by men and women has changed over time.

6

4 'The total consumption by women in 2000 and 2008 were very similar. The proportion of beer decreased but the proportion of wine increased.'

a Why would pie charts be a good choice for illustrating this change?

....

....

....

b Draw pie charts to illustrate this information. Show any calculations you do to work out angles.

....

....

....

....

....

....

....

....

....

....

....

....

....

1 Carla wants to find out what factors affect the ability of a student in her school to throw the discus.

She thinks one factor will be age. She will ask about this in a questionnaire.

a List three other factors she could consider.

1 ....

2 ....

3 ....

b Students may not want to give her sensitive information, such as weight.

How could she deal with this in a questionnaire?

....

....

2 This data, showing the ages of young people in a club, is to be shown in a pie chart.

Age	Percentage (%)
11	23
12	30
13	21
14	8
15	18

a Work out the angle of the largest sector of the pie chart.

....

.... angle = ...°

b Work out the angle of the smallest sector of the pie chart.

....

.... angle = ...°

3 Here is some information about the percentages of students getting different maths GCSE grades in two schools.

Grade	Park School	New School
A*–A	17%	25%
B–C	42%	55%
D–E	25%	14%
F–G	16%	6%

a Show this information on a sectional bar chart.

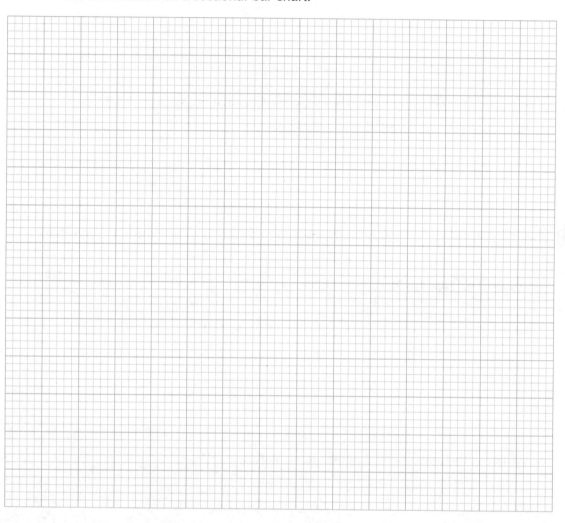

b Molly's father said: 'The chart shows that more students at New School achieved A*–C grades.'

Explain why this statement is not correct. Replace it by a correct statement comparing the A*–C grades.

....

....

....

4 Stuart wants to test whether people who have a good memory also have good reactions. 25 volunteers each do two computer-based tests. Each test gives a score out of 20. The results are shown in this scatter diagram.

Exam hint

Refer to the chart in your answer. You can even write on it if you want to.

a Is there evidence that people with good memories also have good reactions? Give a reason for your answer.

....

....

....

b A score of 16 or more is classed as 'Excellent'. One of the volunteers is selected at random. What is the probability that the volunteer is classed as:

i Excellent on the Memory test ....

ii Excellent on the Reaction test ....

iii Excellent on both tests ....

iv not Excellent on both tests? ....

5 Four identical envelopes contain different amounts of money: 2p, 50p, £1 and £10. Alex takes one envelope and then Reggie takes one.

a List all the possible outcomes.

....

....

b What is the probability that:

i Alex gets £10 .... **ii** Reggie gets £10 ....

iii between them they get £11 .... **iv** between them they get less than £11? ....

c Suppose there was a fifth envelope, containing 10p. How many different outcomes are there in this case? ....

6 In a human fruit machine at a fete, three people each hold up an apple, orange or banana.

a How many different outcomes are there?

.... number of outcomes = ...

b A player wins if all three fruits are the same. Assuming each fruit is selected at random, what is the probability that a player will:

i win .... **ii** lose? ....

7 This table shows the sales of different makes of car by a dealer over six months.

Make	Jan	Feb	Mar	Apr	May	Jun
Proton	8	11	9	12	12	14
Renault	17	15	10	6	7	9
Skoda	12	10	13	16	15	11

a Draw a suitable chart to show how sales have varied from month to month.

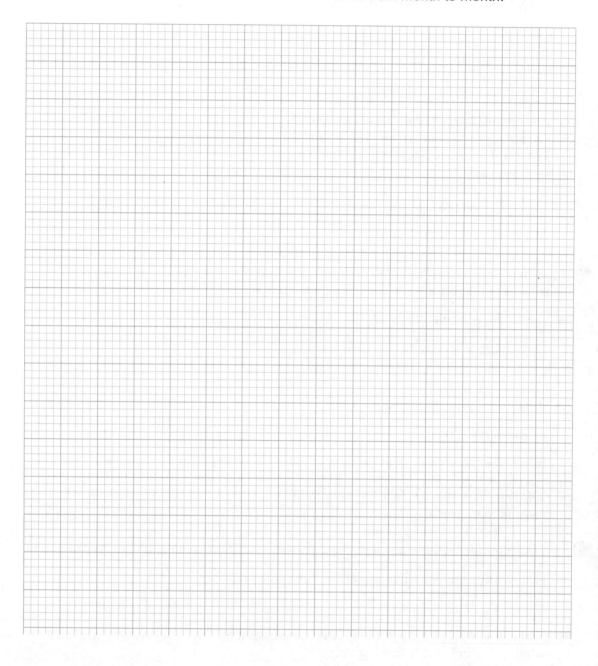

b Which make has shown the greatest variation in sales?

....

8 **a** Two dice are thrown. Draw a diagram to show all the possible outcomes.

b Find the probability that both dice show 1 or 2.

....

....

....

c Find the probability that neither dice shows 1 or 2.

....

....

....

d Beth says: 'Either both show 1 or 2 or they don't, so the answers to **b** and **c** should add up to one.'

Explain why Beth is not correct.

....

....

....

The questions in this section could require you to know the material in any of the previous sections.

1 The four angles of a quadrilateral are x, $x + 10$, $x + 20$ and $x + 30$.

a Write down an equation involving x.

....

....

b Work out the largest angle of the quadrilateral. ....

.... largest angle = ...°

2 This pie chart shows the distribution of the population of the United Kingdom.

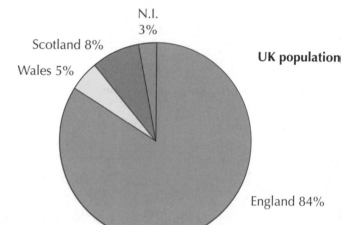

a What fraction of the population of the UK live in Wales? Write your answer in its simplest terms.

....

b Complete this sentence.

The ratio of the population of Wales to the population of the rest of the UK is 1 to ....

c The population of Northern Ireland is approximately 1.8 million.

Use this figure to estimate the population of Scotland.

....

.... population = ... million

d The ratio of the population of England to the population of the rest of the UK is approximately $N : 1$.

What whole-number value of N is required here? ....

.... N = ...

e One person in the UK is chosen at random.

What is the probability that the person does not live in Scotland?

.... probability = ...

3 This is part of a tessellation that extends in the same way in all directions. It is made from squares and equilateral triangles.

a Explain how you know that the angles at any point add up to 360°.

....

....

....

b What is the ratio of squares to triangles in the tessellation?

.... ratio = ... : ....

c The length of the side of each square is 10 cm.
The distance between each row of squares is 8.66 cm.

Work out the area of:

i each square .... area = ... cm^2

ii each triangle .... area = ... cm^2

4 Circular pizzas are sold in two sizes.
Small ones have a diameter of 20 cm and large ones have a diameter of 25 cm.

a Work out the area of each size of pizza, to the nearest cm^2.

....

....

.... cm^2 and .... cm^2

b A notice claims that you get 50% more with a large pizza compared to a small one.
Is this correct?

GO LARGE AND GET 50% MORE!

Show any calculations you do to support your answer.

....

....

c A large pizza is cut into four slices.
Work out the perimeter of each slice.

....

.... perimeter = ... cm

5 A piece of wood is in the shape of a cuboid with a square end of side 5 cm. The volume of the piece of wood is 600 cm^3.

   a How long is it? ....

   ....

   .... length = ... cm

   b Calculate the surface area of the piece of wood.

   ....

   .... surface area = ... cm^2

   c The piece of wood is cut in half along the dotted line. The cut is parallel to the square end. Work out the surface area of each half.

   .... surface area = ... cm^2

6 The cube of a number is 100 more than the number. Find the approximate value of the number, correct to one decimal place. Show any values you try.

   ....

   ....

   ....

   .... number = ...

7 The nth term of a sequence is $n^2 - n$.

   a Write down the first four terms.

   ....

   b What is the percentage increase from the third term to the fourth term?

   .... %

   c Show that the percentage increase from the 10th term to the 11th term is approximately 22%.

   ....

   ....

8 Mel regularly swims the same number of lengths of a swimming pool.

   At one point in her swim she has completed $\frac{2}{3}$ of her total.

   Five lengths later she has completed $\frac{3}{4}$ of her total.

   How many lengths does she swim all together?

   ....

   ....

   .... lengths

9 Ann is a years old.

   a Betty is twice as old as Ann will be in five years' time.

     Write down an expression for Betty's age.

     ....

   b Carol is three times the age Ann was five years ago.

     Write down an expression for Carol's age.

     ....

   c The total of the ages of the three people is 43 years.

     Find the value of a.

     .... $a =$ ....

10 A cube has a total surface area of 486 cm².

   Work out the volume of the cube.

   ....

   ....

   .... volume = ... cm³

11 **a** Enlarge this shape with the corner
     marked C as the centre and a scale
     factor of 2.

   b Draw the image of the dotted line AB
     on the diagram and label the
     endpoints A′ and B′.

   c What can you say about the length
     and direction of A′B′ compared to AB?

     ....

     ....

     ....

     ....

     ....

12 Two cars pass the start point on a straight track. Each is travelling at a constant speed.

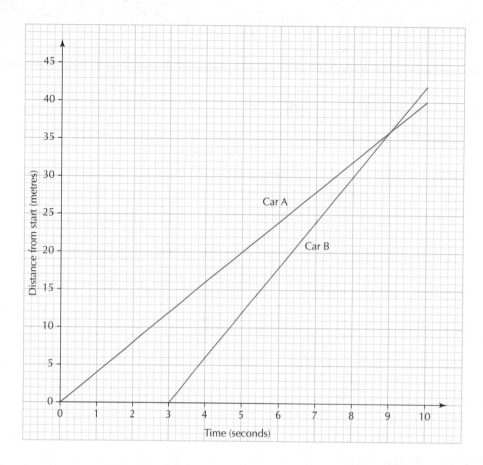

a Work out the speed of car A, in metres per second.

....

....

.... speed = ... m/s

b When did car B pass the start?

....

....

c Find the speed of car B, in metres per second.

.... speed = ... m/s

d How far from the start were the cars when B passed A?

.... m

13 a Complete this table of values for $y = 2x - 4$
and for $y = 5 - x$.

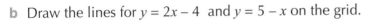

x	-2	0	4	6
$2x - 4$				
$5 - x$				

b Draw the lines for $y = 2x - 4$ and $y = 5 - x$ on the grid.

c The line $y = 2x + 2$ is parallel to $y = 2x - 4$. Draw it on the grid.

d The grid does not extend far enough to show the line $y = 2x + 12$. Where would this line cross:

   i the y-axis ....

   ii the x-axis? ....

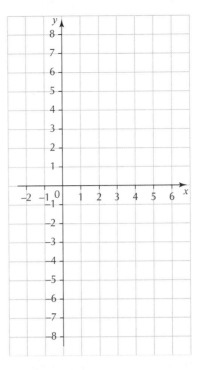

Progression maps

Moving from Level 5 to Level 6

Progression map

Number

Moving from Level 5 to Level 6

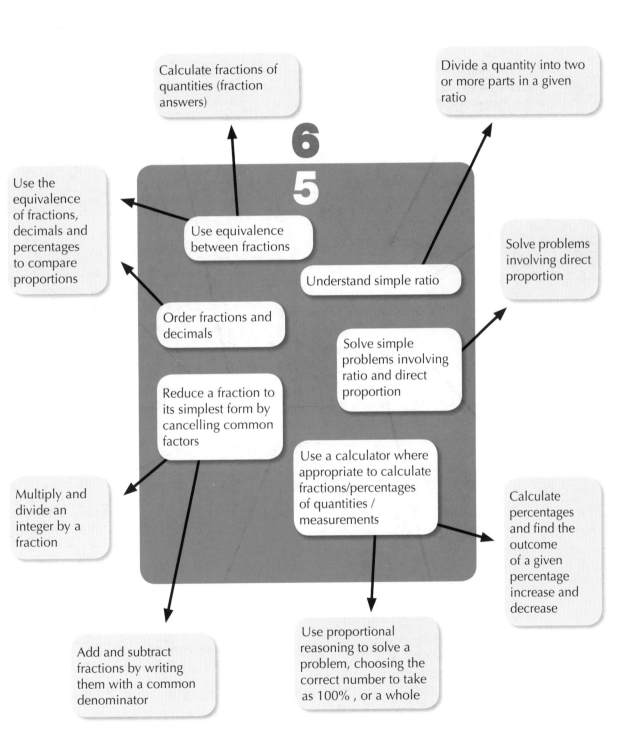

Calculate fractions of quantities (fraction answers)

Divide a quantity into two or more parts in a given ratio

Use the equivalence of fractions, decimals and percentages to compare proportions

Use equivalence between fractions

Understand simple ratio

Solve problems involving direct proportion

Order fractions and decimals

Solve simple problems involving ratio and direct proportion

Reduce a fraction to its simplest form by cancelling common factors

Use a calculator where appropriate to calculate fractions/percentages of quantities / measurements

Multiply and divide an integer by a fraction

Calculate percentages and find the outcome of a given percentage increase and decrease

Add and subtract fractions by writing them with a common denominator

Use proportional reasoning to solve a problem, choosing the correct number to take as 100% , or a whole

Progression map
Algebra
Moving from Level 5 to Level 6

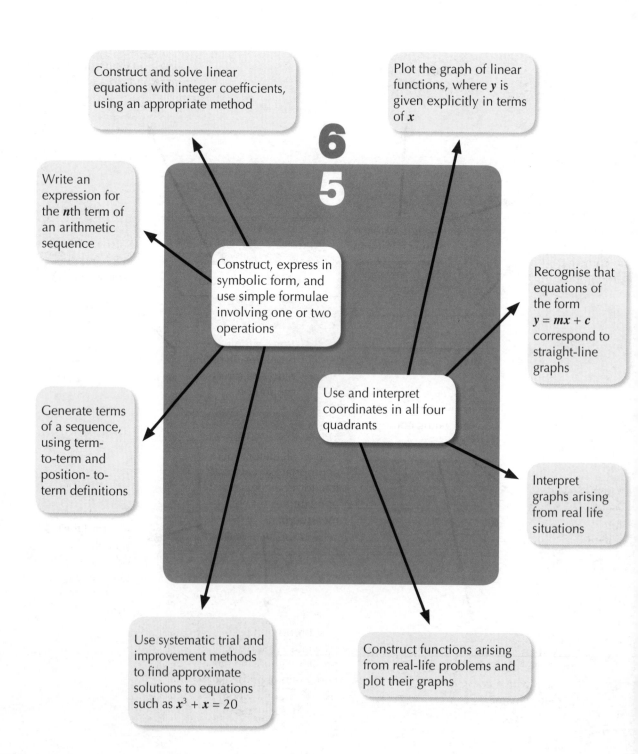

Construct and solve linear equations with integer coefficients, using an appropriate method

Plot the graph of linear functions, where y is given explicitly in terms of x

Write an expression for the nth term of an arithmetic sequence

Construct, express in symbolic form, and use simple formulae involving one or two operations

Recognise that equations of the form $y = mx + c$ correspond to straight-line graphs

Generate terms of a sequence, using term-to-term and position- to-term definitions

Use and interpret coordinates in all four quadrants

Interpret graphs arising from real life situations

Use systematic trial and improvement methods to find approximate solutions to equations such as $x^3 + x = 20$

Construct functions arising from real-life problems and plot their graphs

Progression map
Shape, space and measure
Moving from Level 5 to Level 6

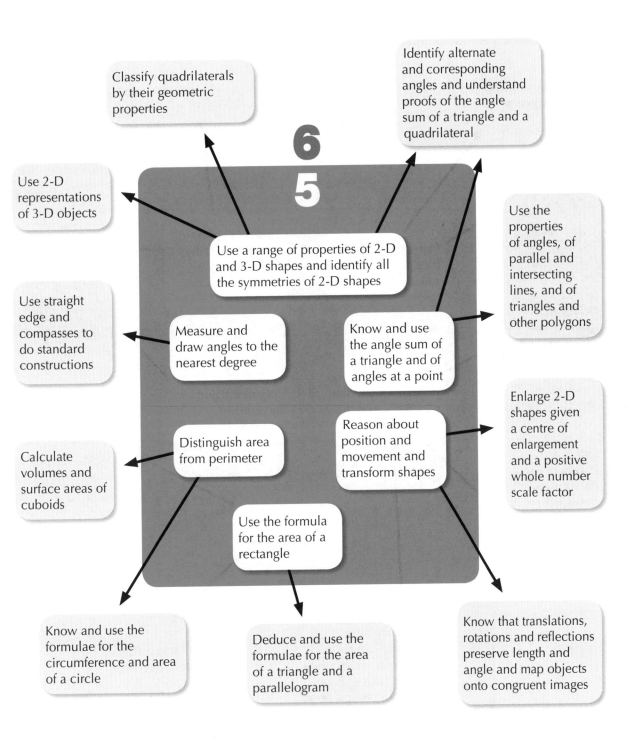

Classify quadrilaterals by their geometric properties

Identify alternate and corresponding angles and understand proofs of the angle sum of a triangle and a quadrilateral

Use 2-D representations of 3-D objects

Use the properties of angles, of parallel and intersecting lines, and of triangles and other polygons

Use a range of properties of 2-D and 3-D shapes and identify all the symmetries of 2-D shapes

Use straight edge and compasses to do standard constructions

Measure and draw angles to the nearest degree

Know and use the angle sum of a triangle and of angles at a point

Enlarge 2-D shapes given a centre of enlargement and a positive whole number scale factor

Calculate volumes and surface areas of cuboids

Distinguish area from perimeter

Reason about position and movement and transform shapes

Use the formula for the area of a rectangle

Know and use the formulae for the circumference and area of a circle

Deduce and use the formulae for the area of a triangle and a parallelogram

Know that translations, rotations and reflections preserve length and angle and map objects onto congruent images

Progression map
Handling data
Moving from Level 5 to Level 6

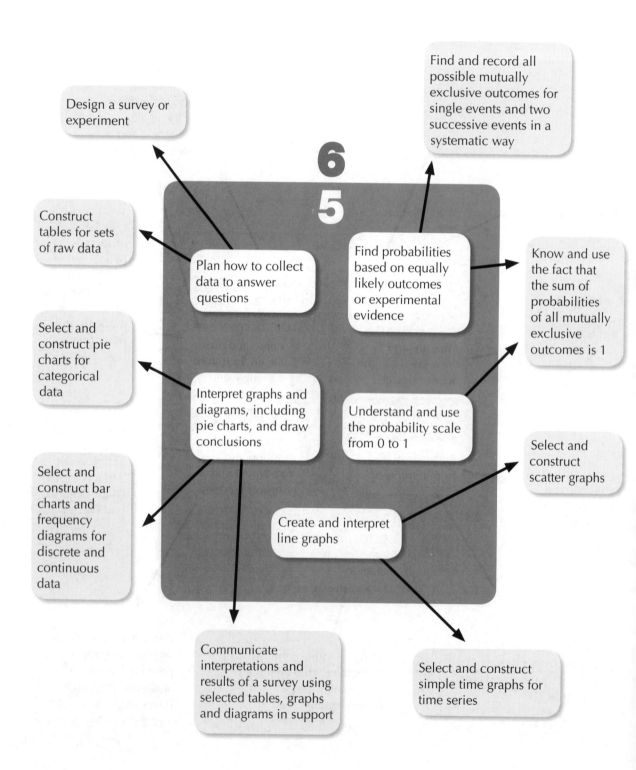

Design a survey or experiment

Find and record all possible mutually exclusive outcomes for single events and two successive events in a systematic way

Construct tables for sets of raw data

Plan how to collect data to answer questions

Find probabilities based on equally likely outcomes or experimental evidence

Know and use the fact that the sum of probabilities of all mutually exclusive outcomes is 1

Select and construct pie charts for categorical data

Interpret graphs and diagrams, including pie charts, and draw conclusions

Understand and use the probability scale from 0 to 1

Select and construct scatter graphs

Select and construct bar charts and frequency diagrams for discrete and continuous data

Create and interpret line graphs

Communicate interpretations and results of a survey using selected tables, graphs and diagrams in support

Select and construct simple time graphs for time series

6
5

Answers

Number

1 Percentages

1. a £7.50   b 25 kg   c 61.5
   d £17.50   e £2.25   f 300

2. a £12.04   b £116.80
   c £157.50

3. a 120   b 920

4. a £54   b £234

5. a £350   b 52.8 kg

6. a £360   b £1440

7. a £21   b £57.60

8. a £7.90   b £73.75

9. It is incorrect. 40% off £179.99 gives £107.99 and the sale price is more than that.

10. Television: Less. 25% is £131.25 and the reduction of £75 is less than this. Computer: More. 25% is £162.25 and the reduction is £200. Camera: Less. 25% is £71.25 and the reduction is only £56.

11. 30 000

12. a 20% of £400 = £80 and 400 + 80 = 480

    b This time the increase is 20% of £480 = £96 and 480 + 96 = 576

13. £24

2 Fractions, decimals and percentages

1. $0.58 < 0.6 < \frac{2}{3} < \frac{3}{4}$

2. a $\frac{7}{10}$ b $\frac{1}{20}$ c $1\frac{1}{5}$

3. a 0.8   b 0.14   c 3.25

4. a $\frac{4}{5}$ b $1\frac{1}{2}$ c $\frac{1}{40}$

5. a 40%   b 37.5%   c 66.7%
   d 44.4%   e 70.8%   f 15.6%

6. a 40%   b 63%   c 17.5%
   d 7%   e 140%   f 225%

7. a $\frac{3}{5}$ b 40%

8. a 38%   b 62%

9. The percentage unemployed in Aberdale is 22.1% and in Berryton it is 18.4%. The newspaper is incorrect.

10 They could be. One in three is actually $33\frac{1}{3}\%$ but it is close to 30%. If 30% say yes, then 70% could say no because 30 + 70 = 100. That would only be true if there were no 'don't know's.

11 West stand 29%, Centre stand 22%, East stand 14%

12 92%

13 Painting 43% increase; Table 22% decrease; Vase 131% increase

③ Ratio

1 8

2 2 to 3

3 105

4 120

5 150 g

6 **a** Arturo £120; Bella £480
   b $\frac{1}{5}$ **c** 80%

7 **a** First £2500; second £1500; third £1000

8 **a** 18   **b** 2 : 3

9 **a** $\frac{3}{10}$ **b** 40%

10 Alice 27; Zeta 54

11 3 : 2 : 1

12 **a** 3 : 1   **b** 13 : 7

④ Proportional reasoning

1 40%

2 18 km

3 10.5% (or 11%)

4 £25 200

5 60 million

6 **a** 4.5%   **b** 6.0%   **c** 10.3%

7 1250 g pasta; 5 eggs; 750 g tomatoes

8 **a** 20 g   **b** 1.56 litres

9 **a** 5.5 litres   **b** 250 ml

10 £60

11 £7500

12 **a** 13   **b** 65 litres

13 24 minutes

⑤ Calculating with fractions

1 **a** $\frac{2}{3}$ **b** $\frac{3}{8}$ **c** $\frac{3}{4}$

2 **a** $3\frac{1}{2}$ **b** $1\frac{3}{4}$ **c** $5\frac{1}{3}$

3 **a** $\frac{3}{4}$ **b** $\frac{7}{8}$ **c** $\frac{9}{10}$ **d** $\frac{13}{24}$

4 $\frac{5}{12}$

5 $\frac{1}{3}+\frac{1}{5}=\frac{5}{15}+\frac{3}{15}=\frac{8}{15}$

6 $4\frac{1}{4}$

7   **a** $1\frac{3}{8}$ **b** $1\frac{1}{4}$

    c $2\frac{1}{6}$ **d** $1\frac{13}{24}$

8   **a** $\frac{1}{12}$ **b** $\frac{7}{8}$ **c** $\frac{19}{24}$

9 $\frac{7}{12}$

10   **a** $3\frac{1}{3}$ **b** $3\frac{3}{4}$

     c $2\frac{3}{5}$ **d** $2\frac{3}{4}$

11   **a** $5\frac{1}{3}$ **b** $19\frac{1}{2}$

     c $5\frac{2}{5}$ **d** $3\frac{3}{4}$

12 $3\frac{1}{3}$

13   **a** $3\frac{3}{4}$ **b** $2\frac{2}{5}$ **c** $3\frac{1}{2}$

14   **a** 6   **b** 8   **c** $7\frac{1}{2}$

15   The division means 'How many halves make 6?' Two halves make one whole so 12 halves make 6.

16   Carla is correct. $\frac{2}{3}$ is twice as big as $\frac{1}{3}$ so therefore the number of $\frac{2}{3}$ s that make 4 will be half the number of $\frac{1}{3}$ s that make 12.

Review – mixed questions on number

1   Albury has increased by 3100 or 91%; Bishford by 5900 or 15%; Calsten by 4700 or 37%. Albury has the smallest numerical increase and Bishford the largest but it is the other way round if we look at percentages. Albury has the biggest percentage increase and Bishford the smallest percentage increase.

2   **a** $\frac{1}{6}$, $\frac{1}{12}$ and $\frac{1}{20}$

     b The denominators are 2×3, 3×4 and 4×5. The next ones will be 5×6 and 6×7 to give $\frac{1}{30}$ and $\frac{1}{42}$.

     c The fractions become $\frac{5}{6}$, $\frac{7}{12}$ and $\frac{9}{20}$.

3   **a** $\frac{5}{8} = \frac{25}{40}$, $\frac{3}{5} = \frac{24}{40}$ and $\frac{7}{10} = \frac{28}{40}$

     b One possible answer is $\frac{4}{15}$ because the two fractions given are equivalent to $\frac{3}{15}$ and $\frac{5}{15}$. Other fractions are possible.

4   **a i** £235   **ii** £240

     b The increase is £5. The percentage is $\frac{5}{235} \times 100 = 2.1\%$ to 1d.p.

5   **a** 70 miles per hour = 112 km per hour so the speed limit in Britain is higher.

     b Here are some possible values.

miles/hour	30	40	50	70
km/hour	48	64	80	112

6   **a** 40°, 60° and 80°

     b Two values must add up to the third. This is because the other two angles add up to 90°.

Algebra

6 Trial and improvement

1   **a** 5.7   **b** 42.7   **c** 19.8

2   $4.8^2 - 2 \times 4.8 = 23.04 - 9.6 = 13.44$

3   33.75

4   **a** 68

    b 3.5 would be a good choice. The number should be between 3 and 4.

    c 3.5 gives 46.375.

5   5.6

6   **a** The area of a rectangle = length × width

    b 6.7

7   **a** 4   **b** 5   **c** 4.5

8   7.3 cm

9   **a** 21   **b** 3.3

10   **a** 150   **b** 6.4

7 Linear equations

1   $3x + 3$ or $3(x + 1)$

2   $6a - 8$

3   32

4   **a** $a = 13$ **b** $d = 5.5$ **c** $m = -2$

    d $r = 11.5$ **e** $e = -5$ **f** $k = 34$

5   $x = 16.5$

6   $y = 6$

7   **a** $w + 6$

    b Perimeter $= 2w + 2(w + 6)$
       $= 2w + 2w + 12 = 4w + 12 = 4(w + 3)$

    c 3.75

8   132 km

9   **a** $x = 0.5$ **b** $x = 5$ **c** $x = 3.6$

10   **a** 122   **b** −20   **c** −40

8 Sequences

1   **a** 19   **b** 27

    c −17   **d** 22

2   **a** 24   **b** 49

3   **a** 34   **b** 14

4   **a** 32   **b** 9th

5   **a** Subtract 3   **b** −14

6   **a** 16   **b** multiply by 3 and add 4

7   **a** 12   **b** 12th

8 Yes. The 8th term is 0 because
$40 - 5 \times 8 = 0$

9 **a** 399   **b** $2n$

10 $3n$, $3n - 3$ and $3n + 6$

11 2, 6, 12, 20

12 The nth term is $2 \times 10^2 = 2 \times 100 = 200$

13 **a** $5n$ **b** $5n - 2$

14 $4n + 6$

15 $106 - 6n$

(9) Straight-line graphs

1 **a** A(0, 4) B(5, –2) C(–2, 3) D(–3, –4)

   b L is $y = -3$ and M is $x = 3$.

2 **a** The missing values are –7, –1 and 3.

   b, d

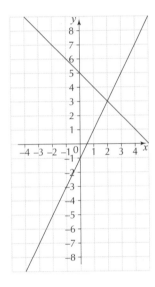

   c The missing values are 8, 5, and 3.

   e (2, 3)

3 **a** The missing values are 1, 2, 4 and 7.

   b The missing values are 7, 3, 1 and –5.

   c

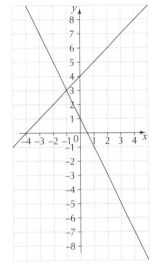

   d (–1, 3)

4 $y = x + 3$, $y = 3 - x$ and $y = 3 + 2x$

5 A is $y = 4 + x$, B is $y = 4$, C is $y = x - 4$,
D is $y = 4 - x$, E is $y = -4 - x$

6 $y = 15$; $y = x + 5$; $y = 2x - 5$;
$y = 3x - 15$; $y = 25 - x$

7 B is $y = 2x + 4$ and C is $y = 2x - 2$

8 $y = 2 - x$ and $y = 4 - x$;
$y = 2 + x$ and $y = x - 4$;
$y = 2x + 4$ and $y = 2x + 2$;
$y = 2 - 4x$ and $y = 4 - 4x$;
$y = 4x + 2$ and $y = 4x + 4$;
$y = 2 - 2x$ and $y = 4 - 2x$

9 **a** C   **b** A

   c E   **d** D

10 **a** $y = x - 2$ **b** $y = 5x$

   c $y = x + 10$

11 **a** A, D and E

   b A and C

   c B, C and E

12 $y = x - 20$

⑩ Real-life graphs

1 **a** $C = 4 + 2D$ **b** £68

2 **a** £40   **b** about £32

   c Yes. The graph shows €80 is worth about £63.

3 **a** 400 m   **b** 5 minutes

   c 10 minutes **d** 10 minutes

6 **a** $C = 5 + T$

   b, c

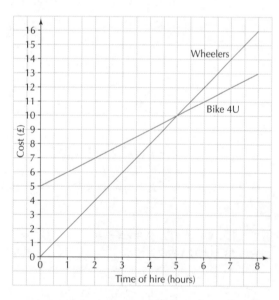

   d They are the same for 5 hours hire. Wheelers is cheaper for less than 5 hours. Bike4U is cheaper for more than 5 hours.

4 **a** 30 km

   b The car stopped for an hour.

   c 100 km

5 **a** 30 minutes   **b** 4 km   **c** 2 km

7 **a**

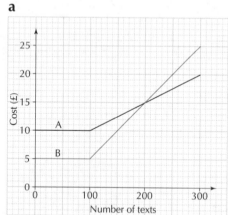

   b Tariff A is cheaper if you use more than 200 texts per month. Tariff B is cheaper if you use less than 200.

8 **a** 10:30am and 5pm

   b 1pm and 3pm

   c 3pm

   d 5 hours

   e 12 noon and 1pm

Review – mixed questions on algebra

1   **a** $3(2n + 5) = 93$ **b** $n = 13$

2   **a** $A + 10 = (A - 10)^2$ **b**   15

3   9.5 cm

4 $6x - 10 = 2x + 18$

    Subtract $2x$ on both sides $4x - 10 = 18$

    Add 10 on both sides $4x = 28$

    Divide by 4 $x = 7$

5   **a**   (10,16) yes; (15,34) no; (–8, –20) yes; (–23, –50) yes

    b   Find the y-coordinate of the point on the line with an x-coordinate of 7.

    c   Find the y-coordinates of points with x-coordinates of 1, 2, 3, etc.

6   **a**   4   **b**   2

7   **a**   The graph is steeper for the first 5 seconds.

    b   45 m

Shape, space and measure

11 Quadrilaterals

1   **a**

    b

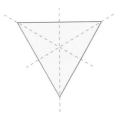

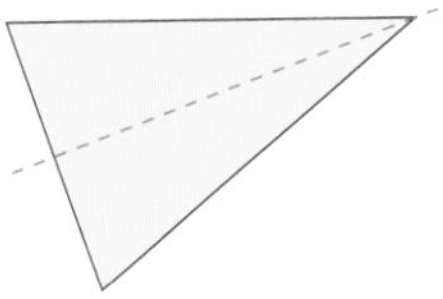

2   **a**   5   **b**   2

3   Kite 1; parallelogram 0; rectangle 2; rhombus 2; square 4

4   **a**   AB and BC; AD and DC

    b   A and C

5   **a, b, c**
The trapezium could look like this.

6   Kite 1; parallelogram 2; rectangle 2; rhombus 2; square 4

7

No equal angles	One pair of equal angles	Two pairs of equal angles	Four equal angles
D	C, H, I	B, F, G	A, E

8

No equal sides	One pair of equal sides	Two pairs of equal sides	Four equal sides
C, D	F	A, B, H, I	E, G

9   **a**   i, ii and iii could be true; iv and v must be false.

    b   The parallel sides of a trapezium will be different lengths.

⑫ Angles

1 $a = 45°$, $b = 138°$, $c = 114°$

2 **a** Both 28°

   b Either both are 65° or one is 50° and the other is 80°.

3 42°

4 **a** 135°

   b

5 **a** Trapezium

   b A = 60°, B = 120°, C = 120°, D = 60°

6 **a** AB = AD because they are both sides of a square and angles B and D are equal. They are both 90°.

   b 50°

7 A = 36°; C = D = 72°

8 Nine

9 **a** 150°   **b** 12

⑬ Geometrical proof

1 The four angles add up to 360°.
   $x = 360 - (90 + 90 + 125)$

2 b; g; f

3 **a** N   **b** X

4 $a = 58°$ (angles on a straight line add up to 180°); $b = 58°$ (corresponding to a); $c = 58°$ (opposite to a or alternate to b).

5 A = 45° (angle sum of a triangle); B = 60° (corresponding angle); C = 75° (corresponding angle or angle sum of a triangle)

6 **a** Alternate angles

   b Alternate angles

7 $a = 40°$, $b = 60°$, $c = 80°$, $d = 80°$, $e = 60°$, $f = 40°$

8 **a** 180°

   b The six angles of the two triangles combine to make the four angles of the quadrilateral.

9 **a** He has included the four angles inside the quadrilateral.

   b Change the last sentence to: 'The angles of the quadrilateral are the same as the angles of the triangles without the four angles at the centre. The angles at the centre add up to 360°. So the angles of the quadrilateral add up to 720 – 360 = 360°.'

10 **a** Alternate angles

   b Because $a + b = e + b = 180°$ (angles on a straight line).

   c Because $a + b + c + d = 360°$ and $a + b = 180°$, so $c + d = 360° - 180° = 180°$.

⑭ Three dimensions

1 6 faces, 8 vertices, 12 edges

2 C and D

3 13

4

5 Cylinder, cuboid, prism

6 **a** 8 **b** 16

⑮ Enlargement

1

2 **a, b**

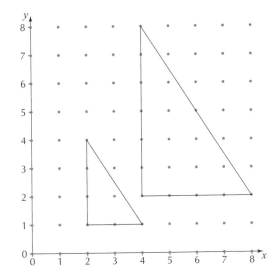

7 Four

8 **a** 7 **b** 15 **c** 5 **d**

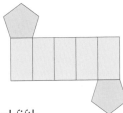

9 The second, third and fifth

10 a d

b

c The angles of each triangle are the same sizes.

d The sides of one triangle are double the lengths of the sides of the other.

3

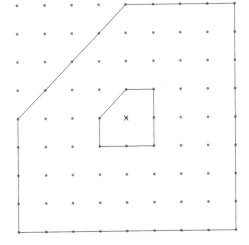

4 **a**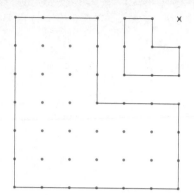

b 24 units

c Because every side of the enlarged shape is three times longer.

5 **a**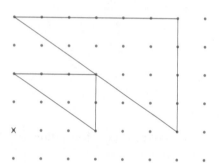

b 6 and 4

c No, the area is 12 squares, four times larger.

6 **a**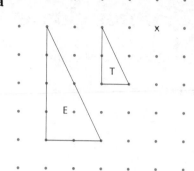

b 2

7 **a, c**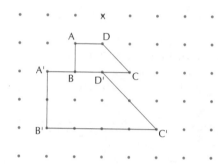

b 2

8 Because the angles are not the same. The triangles are not similar.

9 **a** 1.2 cm **b** 150°

16 Congruence

1 A rotation; B reflection; C translation; D rotation; E reflection

2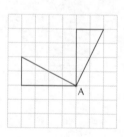

3 B, D, E, G

4 **a, b**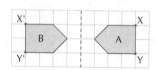

5 **a, b**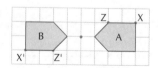

6 a, b

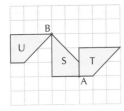

c Translation

7 a, b

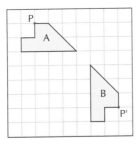

8 a i Yes   **ii** Yes   **iii** No

b W and X are not congruent. (It is similar but not the same width.)

9 a No   **b** Yes   **c** Yes

   d No   **e** No

17 Constructions

1 A = 44°, B = 28°, C = 108°, longest side = 7.3 cm

2 Check by measurement.

3 a Check by measurement

   b 5.6 cm

4 a, b

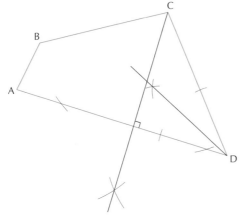

   c 2.6 cm (Allow ±0.2 cm for drawing.)

5 a

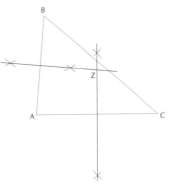

   b They should all be 3.7 cm (Allow ±0.2 cm for drawing.)

6 a

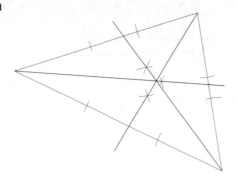

b They should all meet at a one point.
(This is a check on the accuracy of the drawing.)

7 a Check accuracy by measurement.

b 8.5 cm (±0.2 cm)

⑱ Area and volume

1 a A and B; C and D   **b** A and C

2 $\frac{3 \times 4}{2}$

3 a 30 cm²   **b** 5 cm²   **c** 20 cm²

4 a 21 cm²   **b** 35 cm²

5 10

6 120 cm²

7 150 cm²

8 60 m²

9 a 90 cm³   **b** 126 cm³

10 a 336 cm²   **b** 576 cm³   **c** 9 cm

⑲ Circles

1 a 48 cm²   **b** 6 cm

2 a 7.85 m   **b** 4.91 m²

3 a 31.4 cm   **b** 78.5 or 79 cm²

4 a 31.8 cm   **b** 796 cm²

5 46

6 a 82 mm   **b** 531 mm²

7 a 177 cm²   **b** 54 cm

8 151 cm²

9 a 100.5 cm²   **b** 50.3 cm

10 a 70.0 m   **b** 10 200 m² to 3 s.f.

Review – mixed questions on shape, space and measure

1   **a**   Check perpendicular is at right angles to AB with a length of 4.2 cm.

     b   14.7 cm²

2   **a**   72 cm²   **b**   36 cm³

3   There are three possible answers:
$3 \times 4 \times 5$; $2 \times 5 \times 6$; $2 \times 3 \times 10$

4   **a**   60°, 60°, 120°, 120°

     b   23.4 cm²

5   **a**   78.5 cm²   **b**   50 cm²

6   **a**   53°   **b**   96 cm²   **c**   9.6 cm

7   **a**   Two octagon angles and a right angle meet at each corner and add up to 360°. Each octagon angle is half of 360° − 90°, which is 135°.

     b   Combinations of 60° and 108° cannot be put together to make 360°.

8   **a**   150°   **b**   B and E

     c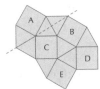

Handling data

20 Surveys

1   a Some possible reasons are: the cars may not be there; other people may park outside a house; people may not park outside their own houses.

   b A questionnaire for each house would be a better method.

2   a 5, 10 and 15 are in two intervals; no group for more than 20 cm; no group for less than 1 cm.

   b Better intervals would be 0–, 5–, 10–, 15– and 20–, where 0– means from 0 to 5 but excluding 5, and so on.

3   a Teenagers is one possible group.

   b At a secondary school is one possibility.

4   a 200   b 250

   c Girls. There was a larger proportion of girls in the 'less than 1 minute' group and a smaller proportion in the 'more than 2 minutes' group.

5   Lots of possible answers. Groups should cover all ages from 18 upwards and every age should be in just one group.

6   Male: 3, 5, 2, 1; female: 1, 2, 5, 1

7   a Some of the data is not relevant. Rows could be either age or school year. Columns could be hours spent on homework, grouped in an appropriate way

   b One possible question is: 'Does the number of brothers and sisters you have affect the time spent on homework?'

21 Representing data

1   a Africa

   b Not possible to say

   c 25%

2   a 7

   b Bus 3. The column for bus 3 has the longest section for women.

3   a A pie chart or bar chart

   b A bar chart or pie chart

   c A time graph

4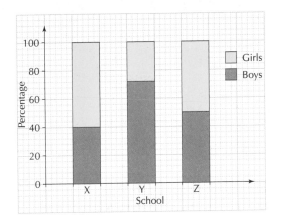

The graph must include a key.

5 Angles are: A 48°, B 160°, C 120° and D 32°

6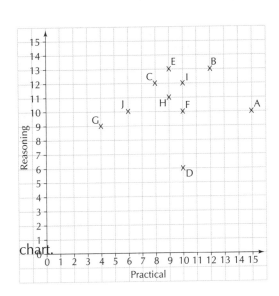

chart.

Axes could be the other way round.

7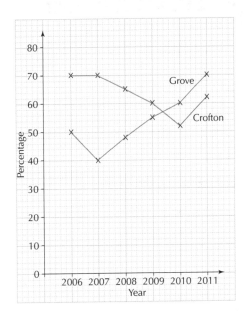

8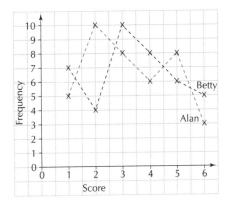

This is one possibility. Others include two pie charts or a comparative bar

22 Outcomes

1 a $\frac{1}{10}$ **b** $\frac{2}{5}$

  c $\frac{1}{2}$ **d** $\frac{6}{25}$

2 a $\frac{7}{20}$ **b** $\frac{7}{20}$ **c** $\frac{1}{5}$

3 a 1, 4, 9, 16, 25, 36   **b** $\frac{1}{3}$

4 a 1 and 2, 1 and 3, 1 and 4, 2 and 3, 2 and 4, 3 and 4

  b $\frac{1}{6}$ **c** $\frac{1}{2}$ **d** $\frac{2}{3}$

5 a

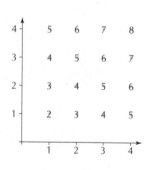

  b 7

  c i $\frac{1}{16}$ **ii** $\frac{1}{8}$ **iii** $\frac{1}{4}$

6 The four equally likely outcomes are HH, HT, TH and TT. There are two ways to get 1 head and 1 tail.

7 a

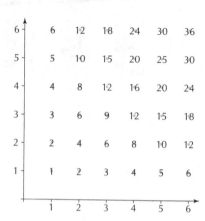

  b i $\frac{1}{18}$ **ii** $\frac{1}{12}$

8 a H1, H2, H3, H4, H5, H6, T1, T2, T3, T4, T5, T6

  b $\frac{1}{4}$

9 a AX, AY, AZ, BX, BY, BZ, CX, CY, CZ

  b i $\frac{1}{9}$ **ii** $\frac{2}{9}$ **iii** $\frac{4}{9}$

23 Probability

1   **a** 0.32   **b** 0.44   **c** 0.24   **d** 24%

2   **a** 0.4   **b** 0.6   **c** 0.7

3   **a** 95%   **b** 35%   **c** 20%

4   Green and yellow are both 0.15.

5   **a** 68%   **b** 12%

6   **a** $\frac{35}{36}$ **b** $\frac{25}{36}$ **c** $\frac{1}{36}$

   d $\frac{5}{18}$ **e** $\frac{25}{36}$ **f** $\frac{25}{36}$

7   **a** 0.96   **b** 0.63

8   **a** 40%   **b** 95%   **c** 35%

9   **a** 80%   **b** 45%   **c** 15%

10   **a** $\frac{15}{16}$ **b** $\frac{5}{16}$

   c $\frac{1}{4}$ **d** $\frac{3}{8}$

11   Assume the pattern continues. The probability of no heads with 5 coins is $\frac{1}{32}$. So the probability of at least one head is $1 - \frac{1}{32} = \frac{31}{32}$.

24 Interpreting data

1   **a** Cannot decide   **b** True   **c** Cannot decide   **d** False   **e** Cannot decide

2   A sectional bar chart would be a good choice.

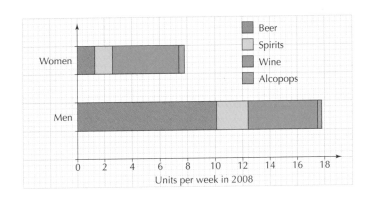

3 A time chart would be a good choice.

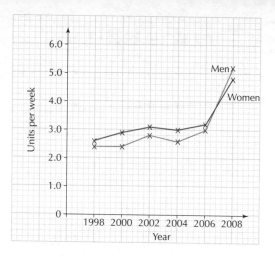

4 **a** Pie charts are good for showing proportions.

b The angles for 2000 are 109°, 87°, 132° and 32°. The angles for 2008 are 60°, 60°, 222° and 18°.

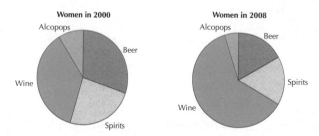

Review – mixed questions on handling data

1 **a** Others could be height, weight, gender, fitness, etc.

b Make it anonymous.

2 **a** 108°   **b** 29° (28.8°)

3 **a**

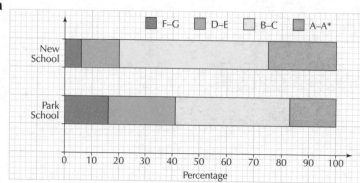

b The chart does not show numbers, it shows proportions. The chart shows that a greater proportion of students at New School achieved A*–C grades.

4 a Yes. All the people with a high memory score also have a high reaction score.

b i 0.28 **ii** 0.16 **iii** 0.12 **iv** 0.88

5 a

Alex	2p	2p	2p	50p	50p	50p	£1	£1	£1	£10	£10	£10
Reggie	50p	£1	£10	2p	£1	£10	2p	50p	£10	2p	50p	£1

b i $\frac{1}{4}$ **ii** $\frac{1}{4}$ **iii** $\frac{1}{6}$ **iv** $\frac{5}{6}$

c 20

6 a 27 **b i** $\frac{1}{9}$ **ii** $\frac{8}{9}$

7 a A time chart would be most suitable.

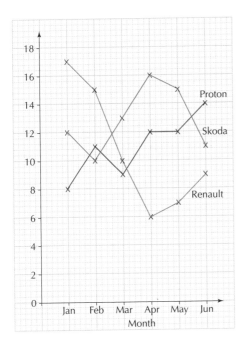

b Renault

8 a Something like this would be suitable.

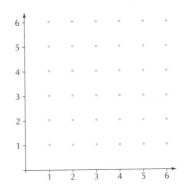

b $\frac{4}{36} = \frac{1}{9}$ **c** $\frac{16}{36} = \frac{4}{9}$

d There is also the possibility that one shows 1 or 2 but the other does not.

Review – mixed questions for level 6

1 **a** $x + x + 10 + x + 20 + x + 30 = 360$ or
$4x + 60 = 360$

  b 105°

2 **a** $\frac{1}{20}$ **b** 1 to 19

  c 4.8 million

  d 5   **e** 92% (or 0.92)

3 **a** At each corner three angles of an
equilateral triangle and two angles of
a square meet. These add up to
$3 \times 60° + 2 \times 90° = 360°$.

  b 1 to 2   **c i** 100   **ii** 43.3

4 **a** 314 and 491

  b It is true. You actually get more than
50% more. 50% of 314 = 107 and 314
+ 107 = 417 which is less than 491.

  c 45 cm (or 44.6 cm)

5 **a** 24 cm   **b** 530 cm²   **c** 290 cm²

6 4.7 because $4.7^3 - 4.7 = 99.123$ and
$4.8^3 - 4.8 = 105.729$

7 **a** 0, 2, 6, 12   **b** 100%

  c 10th term = 90; 11th term = 110.
Increase is 20 and $\frac{20}{90} = 22.2\%$

8 60 lengths

9 **a** $2(a + 5)$ **b** $3(a - 5)$ **c** 8

10 729 cm³

11 **a, b**

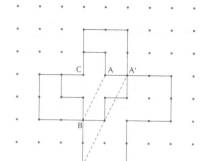

  c A′B′ is double the length of AB and
parallel to it.

12 **a** 4 m/s   **b** After 4 seconds

  c 6 m/s   **d** 36 m

13 **a**

x	–2	0	4	6
$2x - 4$	–8	–4	4	8
$5 - x$	7	5	1	–1

  b, c

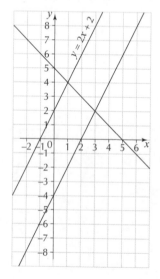

  d i (0,12)   **ii** (–6, 0)